EMPTY

SUITORS

*A woman's caffeinated journey through a
year of dates and self-discovery*

By

Mia Chediak

Printed in the United States of America

First Printing, 2017

ISBN: 978-0-9986372-1-1

Acknowledgement

Special thanks to my wonderful editor for his patience and understanding. Without him, this book would not have been written.

Table Of Contents

To My Mother

For always believing in me and being the finest example of what it means to be a woman

PROLOGUE

I never used grocery delivery services because I assumed the clerk filling the order would give me all the produce that was wilted, meat about to go bad, and the dented canned goods that gave people botulism. Letting someone else pick your groceries was almost as bad as letting another person pick your dates. In both cases, I was certain someone might try to sneak in subpar product. With my luck, I'd end up with the peach that had a big, brown spot on it, which in human terms, equated to the short, bald guy who still lived in his mother's basement.

Next time, I would choose for myself and not accept the market's day-old bread. Even friends couldn't convince me that fancily packaged items on sale were as good as the ones that were full price. On sale meant something was wrong with it, even if it looked good. I couldn't select based on appearance alone and trust what I was getting. I had learned that firsthand.

At first, I went through the motions without really shopping, except for what was indispensable. I vowed to squeeze and sniff, turn and toss each item before buying, only putting in my cart what I truly wanted and had thoroughly inspected. Trying to be pragmatic instead of the wide-eyed optimist who was easily deceived, I reasoned that I was better off alone than constantly looking over my shoulder, waiting to be hurt again. If my destiny was to push a half-empty cart by myself, so be it. It beat having someone circle around me, picking at the remains. In short order, that became a monotonous routine. Even I had to admit they skipped me when the patience gene was being handed out. I got the impulsiveness one instead. For me, a year of thinking rather than feeling was a lifetime, but being taken for a fool twice was just not my style.

CHAPTER 1

GENESIS

Romantically, I was born in college, where after casually dating a few guys, I met the man I later married. I fell for him immediately, the same way I did everything, but that was eons ago. Boy could he talk, even back then. Built like a jock, with a good brain, and a tender heart, Alan Stoddard was my cocktail of choice. Rather than slowing me down, most of my friends encouraged me by saying that he was quite a catch without even knowing him. People told me I was lucky to have landed such a handsome boyfriend. It seemed I wasn't the only one smitten with his chiseled features, blue-green eyes, broad shoulders and cleft chin. Even my family thought I was trading up, because I wasn't built like a Barbie doll or willing to put in hours doing my makeup and hair. Lisa, sensible even in her youth, was the lone standout who questioned the whirlwind romance. She had pointed out that his looks would fade and cautioned me to make certain there was something worthwhile beneath the gilded surface. Not liking the sound advice she offered, I chose to disregard it and barreled forward. When he proposed after dating me for only six months, I said yes enthusiastically, and we were married right after he graduated.

Alan was three years older and seemed worldly to me. We decided, after he made his preference known repeatedly, that I would drop out of school before graduating. That way, I could work to help him pay for his post-graduate degree. He had become a master at convincing me his preferences would be best for us in the long run. Though it was a sacrifice to put off my education, at the time, it seemed like the logical thing to do.

After interviewing in several different fields, I landed a job as a showroom girl in the garment district. I was hard-working, caught on fast, and became enamored with the fast pace of the business world. Determined to succeed, I muscled through mountains of work each week and was promoted several times before my husband got his MBA. My intention had been to go back to school as soon as his career was established, however, even with his fancy title, his not so fancy paycheck wouldn't allow for that. Alan was smart, but never pushed himself or got promoted. He seldom showed up enthusiastically, and once there, he gave his job minimal effort, saving his passion for hobbies, with looking like a matinee idol right at the top of the list. By the time he graduated, I was working as an assistant to the director of marketing for a fashion company and enjoying it. My goal had been to become the department director before I reached the symbolic benchmark of my 30th birthday. School took a backseat to my career and it never seemed like the right time to finish my studies or have children. Focused on ourselves, these things seemed like frivolous extras until it was too late to make them actionable. I was obsessed with excelling at my job and being the perfect homemaker, while Alan was consumed with keeping up appearances, buying a house in the right zip code, and owning the latest toys. We were the last of the yuppie generation and true spokespeople for the children of excess.

When Alan's hairline started to recede and his hair became sparse where it should have been full, and then grew where it didn't belong, he redeemed his self-esteem by taking on extracurricular activities. He set his sights on wooing his young, impressionable secretary and always the charmer, he hit his mark. Even I had to admit she was pretty, but still refused to believe that he was willing to throw away our life together for a meaningless fling. I had always trusted him and envisioned our marriage a safe harbor that would always be my refuge. Dealing with a vain man, I should have seen it coming, but I didn't, and his betrayal eliminated the word trust from my vocabulary.

At first, our life started to unravel without my understanding why it was changing. Acquaintances watched from inside their bay windows as though they were watching a soap opera unfold. Alan finally admitted to bedding his secretary as part of his mid-life crisis and said that despite the affair, he wanted to work things out. I was distraught and looked everywhere for advice on how to handle it. Some people listened sympathetically while acting the part of caring friends. I sensed they were actually more interested in the juicy details of his indiscretion than in being there for me.

Alan and I went for counseling harboring such resentment that the sessions were ineffective at best. Going to therapy for our marriage after everything that had happened was akin to sending a comatose patient to rehab. It was too little, too late. The union survived only because it was kept alive by means of a respirator and force-fed intravenous infusions. To the rest of the world, the relationship appeared to be strong and thriving. People often acted as though we could survive anything, but we both knew better. The marriage would never be whole again. Trying to revive it with half-hearted efforts yielded no positive results. After the first few appointments, which served only to set the stage, our therapist wanted to delve a little deeper. Trying to know us as individuals, she asked him what three things he would take to a deserted island. Alan answered quickly without having to think about it: his hummer (open to your interpretation), his Bowflex machine, and his Gucci loafers. I realized at that moment that his infidelity was merely the issue that brought our many, less dramatic, but equally important ones to a head. Before walking out of the Freudian emergency room, I disconnected the respirator, acknowledging the death of our marriage by closing the door on it. I never turned to look back.

I questioned the Greek chorus about whether or not they had known about the affair. Behind my back, they talked about it, but when confronted, most shrugged and said they couldn't be sure he was cheating while mumbling something about it not being their place to get involved. Now that we were divorced and it got out that his rubbers had hit the road, the same people suddenly became new age protégés of Anne Sullivan - deaf, mute and dumb. They weren't the only ones who had changed. I had changed as well. The experience made me untrusting and cynical. If someone who I trusted and loved could so callously disregard my feelings, how could I expect better from anyone else? From that point on, the choices would be mine and everyone else's opinions meant nothing to me, except of course for Lisa's.

On New Year's Eve, a year and a half after my divorce had been finalized, I found myself wondering what the rest of my life would look like. I had a job and a handful of friends who were important to me, but other than that, my life was empty. For me, it seemed the promise of a happy future was the stuff of fairy tales and though the prospect of starting over was intimidating, I didn't have much choice. The upcoming New Year, coupled with my fear of being alone and filled with sadness, prompted me to finally heed Lisa's valuable advice to move on. Though I'd been out of circulation for what seemed like an eternity, she was right. It was time to turn the page and start a new chapter in my life.

I knew it wouldn't be easy, but had not wanted to admit that many of the impediments were of my own making. I never listened to music released after 1990 and hadn't kept up with the changes of what was socially acceptable. I worried about stupid stuff, like offering to pay my own way, when I should have been worrying about whether a landing strip or full Brazilian was the right way to go. Before I started watching Dr. Phil, I didn't even know what manscaping was. As though not having been with a man other than my husband in years wasn't enough, I had to worry about how it would feel to hold a smooth-chested guy who looked like a pre-pubescent boy.

Once I told people about my decision to date again, they immediately wanted to fix me up with friends of friends. Acquaintances offered me unsolicited advice on how to meet the perfect man. At first, I listened. Then I turned to talk shows and women's magazines for guidance. I'll admit it was not the wisest move. They claimed a "put it all out there" approach was best. The general consensus was that assertive action and bold statements were the easiest way to start dating again, but I had always been reserved. It would have felt weird to hang a shingle. So what if I didn't want to take out a billboard to advertise the fact that was dating again?

I thought about my options for weeks before coming to a conclusion. After finally crawling out of my cave, I decided to get a bachelor's degree in bachelors and to establish myself as an eligible and desirable divorcee using something a little more low-key - the internet. Dating sites seemed like a reasonable way to approach being romantically challenged. By allowing me to hide behind a computer screen, a site provided me with the desired anonymity. I wouldn't feel so exposed online because clicking the computer keyboard felt less intimidating than meeting strangers in a bar. There would be no awkward standing around fidgeting while waiting to be chosen like a 47-year-old debutante at her coming out party. I'd explore romance from the comfort of my living room, in sweats, with the television volume on very low. That way, it would feel like I had company while still being able to focus on the task at hand. Several of my friends in second marriages met their husbands that way. Even the ones who tried it without the desired outcome had some interesting stories to tell about the people they met. Contrary to tabloid headlines, not one of them had been abducted by aliens. Some even met after a series of computer algorithms played Cupid with their data. It sounded playful and frisky to me, but I didn't even want other people matching me up, so I certainly wasn't about to let software do it either. After looking at the options, I decided that Match.com was the appropriate venue for my reintroduction to dating. It afforded me the most control and having that as a safety net was a good thing. I drafted a realistic profile, posted a recent photograph in good lighting, and described myself as honestly as I could, only later finding out that it was the first of my many mistakes.

In my excitement to let Lisa know that I'd decided to test the waters, which for me meant taking the plunge head first, I hastily took a screenshot of my profile, added it to an email with the subject line "Looking to get laid after almost two years of celibacy!" and hit send without checking it first. When emails starting pouring in from coworkers giving me "that a girl" and "kudos", I circled back and realized that I sent the email to the entire team I now directed at Luster Handkerchiefs instead of only to Lisa. So much for anonymity. In a bar, I'd be exposed to several drunken strangers, but now I had advertised myself to a large group of co-workers as "Ms. Shopping for a Boyfriend". When Howard, my boss, chimed in, I knew I'd never hear the end of it. The entire marketing department read about what my dream date would be and how I liked to spend my time. I felt naked and dreaded the thought of people commenting on my sex life, or lack of it, at the water cooler. I made my proverbial bed and now, hopefully someone worthwhile would join me in it.

Lisa reached out later that day and popped over for coffee. When I told her what I'd done, she laughed. "Nice going. Now that you sent out an email blast, you might as well resign yourself to the backlash. You'll have to wear a scarlet 'A' on your forehead forever," she said sarcastically. "You've got to slow down. Haven't you learned by now that rushing will get you nothing other than mistakes?"

"Don't remind me. Hey, you're supposed to be my best friend. Go easy on me. Everyone is entitled to make a mistake," I replied.

"Yeah but you already made yours almost thirty years ago and now you've divorced him. You have to get out of your own way. Take your time and do it right. Okay?"

"You're right as usual. I need to be patient, to take my time and have a plan. I hear you, promise. Come here, let me show you my profile," I said powering up my laptop. As soon as it popped up, Lisa read it and said, "Jules, this isn't right. It doesn't even sound like you. You have to be yourself."

"What do you mean? My profile describes who I am, just without some of the bad stuff."

"Yeah, right - only if you are the reincarnation of Joan of Arc. Stop trying to be who you think everyone wants you to be."

I guess I laid it on pretty thick. Lisa was always a proponent of finding a man who fit your wants and needs by being genuine. She said he was going to see the real you in the long run, so you might as well be yourself from the start. Lisa loved her husband Joey and often commented that he knew her better than she knew herself. She claimed that was why the marriage worked so well.

"If I could do it all over again, I'd still pick Joey," she said as though hearing my thoughts.

"That's not what you said last week. Remember how pissed you were because he wouldn't even take out the garbage?" I chimed in.

"Yeah, yeah, so he's human. He has his moments, but is a really good husband and a great father. Besides, he can still rattle my cage in bed," she smiled and looked aside devilishly, as if remembering a juicy detail and not wanting to make me jealous.

We'd gone to high school with Joey and they kept dating after that. Lisa had always seen something special in him and felt he was a true find from the start. Even at twenty, she said her friends would envy her someday. Their marriage was solid and their love grew stronger over the years. Of course, it didn't hurt that he held up well and could still catch someone's eye. Even better than that, Joey never seemed to notice when other women looked at him, and he never looked around himself. They had always been happy, although even they had highs and lows. Lisa had been right about him. Even now, she was envy of all her friends when her husband told her how pretty she looked. He still reached for her hand as though they were newlyweds after two decades of marriage and her eyes welled up with proud tears when she spoke about her love for him.

Lisa understood me better than anyone else and she could always be counted on for sound, honest advice. So, when she spoke, I listened.

"Lighten up your profile. It sounds like you are applying for a job at NASA. If you are, then it's perfect. If not, it is too serious. It's just not you. For now, channel your light-hearted side. Dating has to be fun on the outside, but on the inside, you've got to be very discriminating. Take notice of the warning signs. Examine your needs and appreciate the benefits of a blank slate to write the profile that will attract the man you want. Shed your hang-ups along with your baggage. Then sip a cocktail, slip into a sexy outfit, put on some jazzy music and get in the mood."

"And then?" I asked.

"Then ask yourself what you truly want from a partner. Approach getting the right guy like you would approach ensuring you seal a business deal. Arm yourself by doing the needed legwork and gathering intelligence on your mark. Go undercover if need be. Rally the troops, then with passion, pursue your goal with the stamina and focus of a navy seal."

"Enlist me Admiral. I'm ready to serve my libido."

"Stop kidding. Forget the past, it wasn't that good anyway. Picture the future you want, then draft a blueprint on how to build it from where you are standing right now. Once you've got that figured out, go find a guy who will fit the bill. Present yourself as the successful, confident, experienced and vivacious woman you are."

"Me, really? That's why we've been friends forever. You always say the right thing. Now go away, so I can start revising my profile."

"Not on your life - I'm putting up a pot of coffee and working through this with you. I've got a vested interest you know. I'll be living vicariously through you, so remember that our happiness is paramount and that you have to get laid for two!"

I smiled broadly feigning bravado as she left the room, but as soon as she was out of sight, I trembled at the thought of exposing my jugular. Regardless of that, I listened to her advice. She was usually right. Breathing deeply to stop my heart from racing, I examined my wants and needs as well as the attributes I valued. I drafted my specifications after doing some serious thinking about what I wanted in a guy.

It read:

- A man with similar interests, or who at least was willing to try the things that interested me – for example the theater, travel, literature, and romantic dinners by candlelight
- A man who was attractive. He didn't need to be handsome in the classical sense, just right for me
- A man who had all his senses: a sense of humor, a sense of adventure, and common sense
- A man who was employed
- A man who would embrace being in a committed relationship and be loyal
- A man who was a grown up
- Oh, and since I was writing a wish list, no harm in asking for a man with whom the chemistry would be combustible

My wants didn't read like a desperate cat-lady who was willing to settle for the first man she met, but other than the last requirement, I hadn't reached for the moon either. I had chosen to look for characteristics that were solid as well as desirable attributes, but those traits alone didn't add up to someone I would fall in love with. How could you write an ad for love anyway? There was something magical about it that could never be captured in words. The way I was feeling at the moment, my headline should have read, "Lowered the Bar in Hopes of Finding a Decent Partner." I was sure I'd need to tweak it along the way, but for now I had my outline.

Once I had completed the first task, we began reworking my profile. We combed the internet like an old man on the beach with a metal detector, looking for a gem of a profile to use as a template. Most of the profiles had a lot of fluff and little substance. They were like the cereal aisle, too sugary sweet and more about the packaging than what was inside the box. Some had provocative photographs and lots of innuendos. Not finding a good example, we built my profile ground up, crafting one that suited me precisely. The result was genuine, softened up a bit, and not too flashy. It had a personality, a point of view, creative flair, and sarcastic humor, just like me. When we felt it was perfect, we triple checked it at Lisa's insistence, then posted it.

"Ok, now that you've presented yourself as you are, you have to brush up on your dating skills. Let's hear what you would say to me on a first date," Lisa said.

"I can't practice being sultry and seductive with you. It would feel really weird."

"Who said anything about being seductive? Be yourself," she said as she leaned back in her chair with a self-satisfied expression on her face.

"Why are you sitting like that? You're scaring me. You look like you want me to kiss you."

"No bean brain. Not when you haven't even said hello yet. I'm pretending to be the guy you need to meet. I'm sitting here totally in control, confident and successful. Practice your elevator pitch on me."

"Ok, here goes. 'Hi, I'm Julie. It's really good to meet you.'"

"BO-RING! You have to be a dynamo when you first meet him. Your opening is ordinary and nondescript. If you were applying for a job, HR

14

would throw you into the slush pile without taking a second glance. Make an impression in the first few minutes or else you're toast. Try something like this: 'I've been so busy lately that this is my first chance to relax in weeks. Who needs coffee? What I really need is a dirty martini!'"

"And to get laid," I giggled.

"Not before you finish your coffee. You can't appear desperate. Get to know the guy before you get to know his dick. Take your time, but be your bubbly, beautiful self, and make sure to let your wonderful intellect and humor shine through."

"Will you marry me?"

"Relax. You will meet me with balls if that's what you are looking for," Lisa said.

"Since I'm putting in my order, can I get a five o'clock shadow too? You know, the last time I even thought about getting into a relationship, I was in college and wanted a guy who looked great in his jeans, owned a cool car, and made me laugh."

"There you go. Nothing has changed."

"Don't mess with me. I'm out of practice and scared. What if I don't pick the right guy again?"

"Stop getting ahead of yourself. Nobody's picking anybody just yet and in case no one told you, the choice is not only yours."

That weekend, I shopped for a boyfriend online, just like people shopped for everything else. It was fun to read the profiles and see what kind of men were available. The first night, I got winks from two guys whom I didn't find attractive, but was still flattered to be singled out. I made a list of the men I was most attracted to. Thinking about it more carefully, I ditched that strategy. Super-hot guys would be looking for flashy women that could be likened to hood ornaments on sports cars. I was a reliable old clunker with a great engine and had posted a profile with substance. I wanted a man who would love me as I was, but in contrast to that, I was eyeing guys who would make my hair curl just by looking at their pictures. My approach wasn't going to work. If I wanted a guy who would value me for who I was, I would have to start looking at men differently too - and maybe even reading their profiles.

My profile got winks from several more guys during the first week. The back and forth flirting was kind of fun. It was exciting to check my phone throughout the day to find a couple of texts or an occasional email. This dating thing wasn't so bad after all. Since I was just starting and still somewhat unsure of myself, I put on my training wheels and made a couple of coffee dates for the following week. It seemed like the right way to go. I needed to be sharp to ensure that beer goggles weren't dulling my senses. Coffee wouldn't involve a huge time commitment in case the guy was a body-double for Quasimodo or looked like a stand-in from Easter Island. People chatted casually with strangers while drinking it. I could be one of those people. To onlookers, I would be an outgoing Manhattanite, warm and engaging, even while having coffee.

I became a regular at Starbucks although candidly, I preferred the cheaper, far more aromatic Dunkin Donuts brew. The trendier coffee house was closer to home, had the right ambiance, and seemed to be everyone else's preference. After several visits, the counter boy already knew me by name. From behind the counter, Isaac would wink, then smile as he handed me my cappuccino. Apparently, he'd seen this scenario play out before. A middle-aged woman, with a different guy each time – yep, I was yet another match in the matchbox called Manhattan. I felt he was passing judgment on me. Although I didn't like it, I tried not to let it bother me, especially since Isaac took his job too seriously. When it came to my dates, he acted as though he was concocting a love potion. "A dash of ginseng in the gentleman's tea?" he asked teasingly. I pretended not to understand. Where did he come off making light of my divorce imposed celibacy? He couldn't have been a day over 26 and stood about 5'4". He had a massive attitude. Because he was short and I tall, eye level for him was where my breasts used to be when they were perky. Though we seldom made eye contact, his hazel eyes were beautiful, but when you looked at him, they were not what stood out. The freckles and the reddish brown mussed-up hair were what you noticed first. He was obviously trying to work a look, though not quite pulling it off. Isaac was friendly in a sarcastic way that was too familiar, sometimes patronizing, and always condescending. He said he was a "barista" by trade. While he thought himself important, it seemed he had no future. It was almost as though he was trying to even the score for all the times he'd been shortchanged, but that wasn't what bothered me most about him. What irked me was how he used his authority, if you want to call it that, to put everyone else down. He did it just enough to make people wonder if he was serious, but not enough to make his manager act on his impulse to flog him in front of Lincoln Center at high noon.

I started out setting up dates sparingly. Not finding what I wanted immediately, I stepped it up. My life became a marathon of coffee dates. Still not getting the results I longed for, I marched my super-caffeinated self through three dates a week, sometimes two in a single day. I practiced my canned intro and selected a go-to outfit that accentuated the good and hid some of the bad. Most of the time, I wore a simple V-neck sweater, dangly earrings, fitted jeans and sensible shoes. The look fell just short of ravishing from my point of view. To finish up the ensemble, I would mist perfume lightly into the air, and walk through it the way French film stars recommended, so it wouldn't be overpowering. What a waste. Wasn't more always better? I usually applied a little light makeup, dramatic only around the eyes and on the cheeks. My cheekbones had to be there, but were tough to find hidden behind the extra padding. Where had my lashes gone? A younger me enjoyed feather-duster lashes too long to wear mascara because it would always dot my brows when I looked up. Finding them now required a ten-time magnifier, but I digress.

The dating scene had changed dramatically. It was all about marketing and exposure. Experts said a personal brand statement was important for online success. What the hell were they talking about? I didn't even know I had a brand, but as a marketing executive, I knew that if I had one, it would need to be marketed in the right way or not at all. Trying hard to make the right impression, I became self-conscious of my every move. I'd run to the corner fast food place to grab a bite and disguise the contraband by dropping the guilty pleasure into a Whole Foods bag. My brand needed to represent a healthy, fresh lifestyle instead of what it was - mass produced with chemical additives to keep me well preserved.

I often felt as though I'd been stuck in time, like a mosquito frozen in amber while the world of dating around me had morphed into something far different than I remembered. Now, instant chemistry had been replaced by instant messaging. Texting had made the one-sided conversation socially acceptable and people were addicted to being connected 24/7. The thumb had always been what differentiated us from animals and was still the defining appendage. Speechless communication had become our mother tongue and given new meaning to the phrase "I'm all thumbs". Grown men were more comfortable texting, and once even sexting me, rather than speaking. The sexter's date was canceled when I received the trailer of his coming attraction. Had he been over-endowed and super proud, perhaps I could have understood it better. What I received looked like cannelloni that had been sitting on the buffet line for about three days. I couldn't understand why anyone would snap a picture of it. The specimen was shriveled up, limp, somewhat scabby, and irritated around the edges. I promptly replied to the text by saying, *No thanks, just lost my appetite.*

I wasn't sure that I was cut out for dating in the hi-tech age. It was impersonal and a numbers game. To call these meetings dates was a euphemism. Let's call them what they were. They were interviews to see who would make the cut. You'd throw a bunch of men against the wall to see who stuck. The sticky ones were the keepers.

After a couple of weeks of not sleeping, I thought about switching to decaf. I still preferred regular coffee, but needed my beauty sleep and caffeine was getting in the way of that. Isaac swore he could tell what a person needed in their life by their drink of choice. I toyed with the idea that he might be onto something, then remembered I didn't trust his judgment. Done with conforming to expectations and refusing to be manipulated to speak Italian by a glorified counter boy, I always ordered my beverage extra-large, like my imaginary lover's condoms, instead of Venti to spite Isaac. Each time without fail, he corrected me, but I stood my ground to further convince myself that from that day forward, I was going to exercise my free will. I would no longer be coerced into doing anything simply because someone else wanted me to.

I thought of myself as a uniquely mysterious divorcee and chose to ignore the fact that there were millions of me on the isle of Manhattan. Many of us were looking for the same thing. The majority of women wanted a serious relationship and the lion's share of the men wanted only to get laid. The odds were not favorable. The females wanted romance and commitment while the males were looking for a cozy, tight, but infertile nook in which to deposit their sperm. Like turtles, they were open to spawning in the shallowest of beds. Of course, it wasn't right to stereotype men, but let's face it, categorizing them worked because a large percentage of the random sampling comfortably fit into predesignated buckets. A great many of these guys were divorced, saddled with alimony, and often had to pay child support. Their last few shekels were forced to work overtime to get them to the motherlode. For them, the ideal date was a quick slice and a hop in the sack before heading home. Most of these men didn't have the interest, time, or money to spend getting to know someone over dinner.

With a few dates under my belt, I felt more polished in my approach and had become more observant. The art of listening was a lost one. Men had always craved attention, so I followed my animal instincts and listened. Even when some of my dates were rude and took a call or sent a text in the middle of a conversation, I continued to appear interested in what each one had to say. As a result of this, I was usually asked out for a second date. It was as though I was conducting a survey on human nature.

At first, acting interested was a fun experiment, but after a debut month filled with meaningless dates, I was bored to tears. They all started to sound the same. My dates were happy that someone was listening to them and more often than not, they didn't take notice of my blank "deer in the headlights" stare. We were not connecting, but the men were often too self-absorbed to have any clue. Disappointed, they couldn't understand why I turned down a second date without realizing that I was merely going through the motions on the first one. No offense to my wonderful dentist, but why the hell would I be willing to subject myself to yet another unsolicited bout of root canal?

The routine became so time consuming and tedious, that I started vetting out the candidates much more online or by phone before even agreeing to an initial meet and greet. I was about ready to give up hope, when after three weeks of chatting online, I decided to meet a guy for coffee who seemed to have potential and appeared to be as sticky as glue.

CHAPTER 2

EXODUS

Rob was my lab rat. After having a single coffee with a dozen strangers, each one stranger than the next, I vetted him out by chatting casually for a couple of weeks before agreeing to meet. Rob wasn't super attractive judging by his pictures, but I was just taking off my training wheels. He'd be a good guy to practice my newly acquired single footing on.

I finally accepted a coffee date at Starbucks for the following Sunday at 10 a.m. and of course, I couldn't sleep the night before. Obsessing over what to say, I got up at 5:00 a.m. after fidgeting sleeplessly in bed for almost six hours. By the time I was supposed to meet him, my biological clock already thought it was lunchtime. I gave myself a quick once over in the mirror and a spritz of fragrance before leaving.

The coffee house was packed and it took me a minute to locate him. I was pleasantly surprised when our eyes met. His profile photo wasn't a good likeness. In person, he was more attractive than expected. My date was a 52-year-old investment banker with a sweet smile and kind eyes. As I later came to learn, he was a catch in the fishbowl of single guys on Match. He was tall, I'm guessing about 6'5"ish, and for the first time in my life, my 5'10" frame felt petite. That alone may have been what gave him the edge. His conversation was somewhat dry and peppered with ums but overall, he seemed smart enough and normal, so I accepted a dinner date for the following Friday.

With lots going on, the work week flew by. In the wholesale industry, the start of the year was prime time and this January market week was no exception. We had a busy appointment calendar through Friday with every store wanting new digital advertising for the coming spring season. Vendors hated market week, but buyers loved it because they were wined and dined in New York's finest restaurants on someone else's dime.

January was lovingly referred to as the tin-cup market. It was when every self-respecting retail buyer reviewed the season and then promptly began to blame his resources for each of his retail woes. They would come to Manhattan in droves, tin cup in hand, tail between their legs, then proceed to give you a canned speech which sounded something like this: "Your product did not perform as expected, so I need help to subsidize your program's margins to make my departmental goal." After having been adamant that these were the styles they wanted to order despite our recommendations, all of a sudden, we were partners in the programs they had selected. Market weeks were like a massive group baptism. Clients from all over the country would descend on New York, get their markdown money, and then as we all held hands, it was as though every bad selection the retailers made had been washed clean. In the industry, we'd laugh about it because the buyers were as dependable as the swallows at Capistrano. It was a sure bet they'd come home to roost.

That Friday morning, I was running late and took the A train down to Herald Square. It was packed. Coincidentally, "the beauty" hired to sit at the reception desk to greet the buyers as they came in, was on the same train. She had gotten pissed off at me when I told her not to pal around with the salesmen from out of town. Madeline was a striking young woman, but wet behind the ears and easily offended. She had come to New York from Canada to become a model and was only doing this in the interim to help pay the rent. Our CEO Howard, drooled over her and she mistook his attention for professional interest. He said he wanted to give her the opportunity to climb the corporate ladder. I imagined his ladder was short and stubby, but she was clueless. I warned her that in order to be taken seriously, she'd have to stop being so friendly to every sperm donor in the building, but Madeline didn't recognize good advice when it was given. She thought that no mistakes would stick to her because she was pretty. On a NY subway train smiling like an out of place tourist, while everyone else on the train, including me, stared at the floor or read, she made eye contact with people. She could have won the nomination for New York's newest victim just off the transit truck. I was so focused on her being out of touch with what was happening around her, that I didn't notice the guy behind me standing closer than he needed to be. Madeline kept smiling and gesturing for me to turn around, but I disregarded her, thinking I knew better. Exhausted of watching her head bob towards the right to get me to turn around, I complied and caught a glimpse of the really sleazy looking guy standing directly behind me with a weird look on his face. He appeared to be in pain. She was trying to be helpful, but I remained unfazed until the train jerked forward, and the guy slammed into my back without even saying excuse me. It wasn't until I turned around to give him a nasty look that I realized he was cradling his penis in his hand. Getting caught in the act must have been an aphrodisiac for him because it was then he came all over my skirt. Madeline screamed and ran to me looking mortified, then hugged me. She wasn't a bad kid, just green. Greener myself now, I realized that I had been wrong. The whole time, Maddie was watching out for me and trying to remind me that mistakes did stick, especially ones of this kind.

We stopped at the corner drugstore, the only retailer open at that early hour to get a pair of leggings for me to change into. She was embarrassed and tried to downplay the incident. With newfound respect for her, I jokingly brushed it off by saying, "What's a little sperm between friends." Being caught off guard had stung me and kindly she never brought it up again. From that day forward, we became buddies. I wondered why he specifically picked me to jerk off on, and although I should have been enraged, truth be told, it was a little flattering. If he had been a little more subtle about it, I might have asked if he'd like to have coffee sometime.

With that dramatic start to my day, it could only get better, or so I thought. Rob picked me up at 7:00 p.m. sharp as promised. "We are going to have a great night," he said.

"I've been looking forward to it all week," I replied hoping that he was too busy driving to notice how flustered I was. Even I had to play the game sometimes in order to move the pawns forward. Other than spending some time online and a few minutes over a polite cup of coffee, we were strangers. A quick date had proved to be only enough time to ward away serial killers and eliminate hunchbacks. I'd become a pro at coffee, but a brief meeting was much easier than a real date. Maybe I wasn't ready to start dating for real.

My mind wandered. Since the ink had dried on my divorce decree, I had lost all interest in men until recently. Alan's secretary had dumped him as soon as she found out he was going to be single and truly available. While I felt it was poetic justice, he moved on to other conquests without delay. He dated for instant ego gratification, but never had a serious relationship after we split up. I wondered whether our marriage had ever been about anything other than building his already massive ego.

Back in the moment, I heard my date speak.

"So about me…I'm a dad to two boys, aged 13 and 16. I'm an investment banker, but you already know that. I'm actually pretty good at it and a partner in my firm. What else do you want to know? I'm an open book."

"How long have you been divorced?"

"Whoa lady! Get right to it don't you? A woman who is not afraid to dive in - I like it!"

"I'm sorry. I didn't realize it was too personal a question. I'm new at this." God this is tough!

"Great. No problem. You want to play it old school? Fine by me. You look very pretty tonight. Do you come here often?"

Patronizing asshole I thought to myself.

"Not too often, I'm busy shearing the sheep and making butter, but when I have the time, I like to let my braid down and make a pilgrimage to find my knight in shining armor."

Sarcasm had become my signature scent. It had always lurked beneath the surface as the base note, but these days, it was the heady top note and immediately detectable. Not wanting to make the evening a bust, I tried to change the mood and brightly chimed in, "Where are we going for dinner? I'm super hungry."

"Sure, you are. Free meals really get your juices going, right? You can smell them a mile away," Rob said. "Chicks are always super hungry. What did you do, skip the grocery shopping this week figuring you'd stock up for the winter tonight?"

Was this a date or a beheading? Trying to make a go of it, I said, "Why don't we start over? It would be great if we could enjoy the evening. I'm Julie, nice to meet you."

"I'm sorry. You're right. I didn't mean to be so abrupt. It's just that it takes me a while to trust the ladies. My ex-wife took me for every cent I had ever saved. I had to move back into my parent's house when it was all I could afford. So now, I'm barely making ends meet with massive alimony and child support payments, while she is remarried and living in the house that I paid for with a deadbeat. I know that some women might not take advantage of my generosity but, after my divorce was followed by several dates with gold-diggers, I'm leery of a woman's motives. I'm sorry. Finances are a tough subject for me."

"I didn't say anything about money. You did, but I understand. It must be very tough to feel taken advantage of by someone you loved," I replied trying to soften my response.

"It is, but clearly I've moved on. Now tell me about you."

 Clearly, he had not moved on.

"Not much to tell really. I've just started dating again and am having a good time meeting new people."

"He left you, didn't he? You look sad and tired. What you need is a back rub and somebody's shoulder to cry on."

"No, actually it was the other way around," I said not explaining why to this self-proclaimed savior in accountant's clothing. I looked around trying to dodge any follow-up invasive questions and realized I had no idea where we were. Until that moment, I hadn't noticed he had driven into a residential neighborhood.

"What an interesting spot for a restaurant. Must be cozy," I said trying to ignore the obvious.

"You have no idea. We have arrived! Prepare yourself for a culinary delight in my castle," he said pointing with a flourish to the smallish two-family brick house straight ahead.

"You're right. I had no idea. I'm not entirely sure that I'm comfortable with all this."

"Not to worry," he replied. "My parents live downstairs and I have the boys this weekend, so I have no choice but to behave myself. Then again, I could give the whole crew cough syrup and we could get to know each other."

Danger, danger Will Robinson, this guy had issues. It was as though he had skipped the pilot to jump in mid-series.

He swung the screen door open to a tidy but sparsely furnished house that appeared to be empty. "I'm home," he called up. Thankfully, I heard a reply grunted back.

"Make yourself comfortable," he said walking away. "Would you care for some wine, or perhaps a cocktail?" he shouted from the adjacent room.

Knowing it was best not to play with hard liquor, though a stiff drink might have settled me, I called back, "A glass of red would be lovely if you have a bottle open."

He promptly resurfaced with wine glasses and a small plate. Rob had prepared some cheese and crackers to accompany our wine. Now, he seemed perfectly normal again. Maybe my reaction had been exaggerated because I was nervous and in unknown territory. The evening might have been salvageable if I had jumped to the wrong conclusion.

We chitchatted for several minutes and I had started to feel a little more at ease by the time I had sipped half a glass of wine. Alcohol, the greatest icebreaker in the history of the world, had worked its magic. He looked at his watch and advised, "I'd better get moving. I've got big plans for us starting with a special dinner, thoughtfully prepared by yours truly."

He was full of surprises.

When I asked if he needed help, Rob looked puzzled.

"Of course not. I've got it all under control and just need to finish sautéing the liver and onions. Here," he said as he handed me a book.

What a weird dish to make for a first meal with someone whose taste you didn't know. Yuck, what was he thinking?

"With teenage boys, I figured this would be a good tool. I've written and bound an instructional sex manual for them. Clever, huh? Why don't you make yourself comfortable and flip through it for ideas?"

I tried to hide my horror, about both the meal he was preparing and the manual. Who did he think he was anyway? He was neither a celebrity chef nor a sex therapist, and he had crossed several lines early and often. I was really uncomfortable and should have gone home instead of getting out of the car. There I was, stuck in his house without a car and I didn't even know where "there" was.

The minute he and his gingham apron stepped out of the room, I cautiously opened the book. Lovingly dedicated to his sons, the first chapter was titled "Setting the Stage". It instructed the reader to cook a homemade meal at his place, saying it greased the skids and was cheaper than a motel. It was at that point that I decided to make some skid marks of my own. I quickly, but quietly, let myself out of the house and thanked the dating muses for cell phone service. I used Uber to get a car while walking up the block as stealthily as possible. Waiting for my ride, I ducked into a narrow driveway between two houses to ensure the Galloping Gourmet wouldn't spot me. I was antsy and tried to make a mental note of everything in my line of vision in case something happened. The street, full of tire marks, made me wonder if I hadn't been the first to leave in a hurry. Five minutes later, when my driver pulled up, I jumped in as though making my getaway. Concerned that I'd be caught before being able to flee, I closed my eyes to avoid seeing the impending doom. After a couple of minutes, when my heart stopped racing, I asked the driver, "Where are we?"

He lowered his radio and laughed back, "City Island lady. The message said you're going to the West Side, right?"

I repeated the address I'd typed into the app and noticed a surprised look on his face when he heard it.

"What are you doing here then? You look like you're on the lam," he replied smiling.

"I was on a date."

"What happened? It's kind of early for your date to be over."

I recounted the story, and could see in his rearview that he was laughing as I spoke.

"So, the Frugal Gourmet didn't make the cut, huh? You ladies have to be more careful. There are a lot of jerks out there just waiting to prey on vulnerable people. You're lucky that I just dropped off a passenger close by. Cabs can be hard to find in this neighborhood."

"Nate," he said as he held out his hand in the form of an introduction.

"A very appreciative Julie," I answered.

"Some set that guy had, huh?"

"I didn't have the pleasure of finding out," I giggled back.

The ride home was the best part of the night. Nate gave me his card and said, "I've thought of changing my card from *Driver for Dependable, Safe Rides* to *Damsel in Distress Saver*. You don't know how many times I end up giving chicks like you a ride home. We're neighbors you know. I live a couple of blocks away, so don't be shy about calling for rides. I'm usually on the West Side and only a call away, except for when I get an airport fare."

The fact that he used the word chick instead of old hen got him a generous tip. I was glad he gave me his card and would be sure to call him for future rides.

What a bust the night had been! I'd waited all week to spend the evening with someone decent and it turned out that the driver was better than my date.

Okay, so I had learned that casual light conversation over a cup of coffee was not an automatic precursor to a successful evening. Even a loser could muster up a decent front for thirty minutes at a clip. Going forward, I would need to delve deeper before committing to an evening date. Once home, the first thing I did was edit my list of requirements by adding another bullet to my list:

• No self-proclaimed sexperts

Dating had made me aware of a few things about myself when meeting new people. I would introduce my very best self to the other person's ideal self and then the two were never seen to surface in the light of day again. It would have been easy to fall in love with someone in his finest hour. The trick was finding someone who played close to the top of his game on a fairly consistent basis. My goal became to meet a man whose reality didn't differ dramatically from whom he presented himself to be. I was being honest, wasn't I? Well maybe not a hundred percent, but it wouldn't do me any good to linger on that. I had heard it said that men wanted a lady in the living room, a chef in the kitchen, and a whore in the bedroom. I wanted the same thing - someone who was as clever out of bed as he was in it, a Renaissance man, perfect for every room!

~~Rob: Investment~~ Banker. First bachelor bites the dust.

I wasn't going to let one disappointing date sour me on dating. It was just bad luck and I was bound to make a better selection next time. That evening, I checked my email to find a nice note via Match from a new guy. When I looked him up, his profile made me smile.

Daniel: Graphic Artist, who had posted a great bare-chested picture of himself while shaving, wearing a Santa hat and foam beard. Handsome in a quirky kind of way, just turned 50. Loved jazz, gourmet food, and racquetball.

He was very handsome, obviously creative, and had varied interests. We exchanged several emails and set a date later that week to meet.

Starbucks, Thursday Night 8:00 p.m. Daniel

With the work week almost over, I was happy to have a date and thought of the school night outing as a little present to myself. Before meeting him, I went home to change and freshen up. As was not the norm for me, I was running a little late and ran out the door while still putting on my shoes. I arrived just in time to find myself one of very few customers in the whole place. Getting stood up was not the way I had envisioned my second adventure. My lack of luck was unbelievable. I took a table by the window and entertained myself people-watching while I finished my coffee. At 8:15 a young couple arrived groping each other as soon as they came in. What was it with people and their too intimate public displays of affection? I hadn't known that coffee was such an aphrodisiac. At 8:20 an old guy walked in and went into the restroom. Then, at 8:30, three friends approached the counter chatting away while Isaac rolled his eyes at me. When a half hour had passed and it became apparent that Daniel wasn't going to show, I stood up and started to wipe down my table. I noticed the old guy walking towards me and wondered if he had been in the bathroom the whole time. He must have wanted my window seat because he was coming straight to me, so I cleaned up more carefully before turning to leave.

"You didn't tell me you worked at Starbucks," he said.

"I'm sorry. You must be confusing me with someone else."

"Clever, clever gal. Julie, it is so nice to meet you. I've been waiting here since before eight o'clock hoping you hadn't changed your mind and here you are."

"And you would be…"

"Daniel."

"Daniel?"

"Yes dear, what is it?"

"Daniel? Are you kidding me?"

"What is it dear?"

"How old was the picture you posted?"

"Please, Julie, let's sit and chat."

"Hang on just a minute," I said without sitting. "Why would I sit with you when you lied about the time you got here? Didn't you think I'd notice that you were late and while we're at it, why didn't you tell me that you were pushing 80 instead of 50?"

"Julie, sweetie, where's your sense of humor? Of course I'll address all of your concerns, but let's relax and get to know each other first. Good things take time."

"By the looks of it, you don't have the luxury of time. You may not be around tomorrow," I blurted out.

"Alright then, if you must know, the picture is of my son. I didn't have a recent one of me and I certainly could not take one myself, now could I?"

Apparently, he'd never heard of selfies.

"I was embarrassed to have gotten here late and hoped you hadn't noticed. You're a really good judge of age. I am 78, but I had to meet you. You look so much like my Clara. Would you have come if I told you my real age?"

"Well I did notice you were late, and no, I wouldn't have come had I known you were 78. You lied twice in less than ten minutes. You're not off to a good start. Why should I care that I look like someone you know and who is Clara anyway?"

As I turned to leave, he grabbed my wrist and said pleadingly, "Don't go yet, please. Let me look at you. Clara was my wife of almost 50 years. She passed away 4 years ago. Will you please stay?" He asked with such hope that I couldn't bear to turn him down.

I sat down and forced a smile.

"Of course, Clara was much prettier in her 40's than you are," he said.

Incensed, I stood up for real this time and left. There I was, trying to be nice and spend some time with him, yet he had no problem telling me that I wasn't as pretty as his dead wife. So was this what it had come to, being dissed by an 80-year-old liar. I wondered what tomorrow had in store for me. If this was the benchmark, it could only improve.

Daniel- Graphic Artist

CHAPTER 3

NUMBERS

The dating rules had changed dramatically and so had the players. I didn't know what was fair or foul and had no clue what my dates thought about me. Let's just say no one looked like they had enjoyed the conversation any more than I did. It seemed as though we were all going through the motions. I was certain there were subtle changes I hadn't even noticed yet. Feeling as though brushing up on my social skills before trying it again might be helpful, I thought about what had transpired in my short dating career. The forced conversations were draining and each lousy date was indistinguishable from its predecessor. I felt awful after every bad outing and knew something needed to change in order to improve my batting average. Eager to feel better about myself and my prospects, I decided to join a gym. The endorphins would be as good for my spirits, as the exercise would be for my body. I'd also heard Madeline say that the gym was a great place to meet men and decided it was time to find out for myself. I had everything to gain and only weight to lose.

I joined the gym that she had recommended and found my first morning workout to be painful from the minute it started. When I arrived at 5:30 a.m. there were already lines to use the machines. People really stood in line to do this and unbelievably, some of them actually seemed to be enjoying it.

Apparently, everyone north of 78th street tried to squeeze in some type of exercise before they sat at a desk for ten hours at a clip. It was a great thing, but did they all have to do it at my gym? I waited for a response but none came. Oh right, I was talking to myself. It had become a bad habit. Thankfully, at least this time, I did it was silently.

The gym was really crowded and the foot traffic made it seem like rush hour. Angry to be wasting precious minutes, I marched myself right up to the front desk ready to complain about what a mob scene it was and to ask if there was consistently a time when it was less congested. Before I could open my mouth, the pretty young woman behind the counter spoke while looking me over. "It'll be better by the end of February. I promise. Oh, and if you'd like some advice, get some cute workout clothes."

I was in sweats and a tee while every other woman under 65 was wearing those trendy yoga pants that the status conscious loved. The company that manufactured them had been in the news because any movement in the pricey pants from their newest collection rendered them see through. It had almost put them out of business but apparently, no one had told the crowd at Perfect Fitness. The uniformed throngs, in skimpy thongs which were clearly visible through their pants, smiled at me. Too sleep-deprived to care, I didn't give it much thought. Even though the gym was supposed to be a place to meet people as much as it was a place to work out, I was on a mission and socializing was not part of the deal, unless it was with an unsuspecting potential partner. I developed a go-to routine for weekdays with the goal of getting toned in the most expeditious manner. Within two weeks, it had become second nature and my practiced behavior didn't include time for making any friends.

The guys at the gym in the early morning were mostly older men and altogether too comfortable slamming their free weights on the floor. They probably did it in an effort to draw attention to themselves. Why anyone would want to spotlight biceps that resembled vacuum-packed boneless chicken thighs was beyond me. These guys looked tight in their workout clothes, but I'm sure that like the thighs, once you removed them from the packaging, their skin would spew out into an amorphous mess. It became clear that I had to look somewhere else when the super fit septuagenarian was the top contender. What had started out at least partially as a hunting expedition, had become my routine. Thankfully, it was a good one. Within three weeks, which is the time it takes to form a habit in case you were wondering, I had more energy and my clothes were starting to fit better. At least this mission had yielded a somewhat positive result. Working out helped me get through each day with more energy even though I was getting up an hour earlier than before.

I put dating on ice for a couple of weeks, using the time to get in shape and hoping it would become easier or that the delay would change my luck. In order to meet the right guy, it became clear that getting back in the game would involve venturing outside of my comfort zone since he wasn't a member at my gym. Even I could see that the trek from home, to the gym, then to work, and finally back to bed didn't hold the key to my romantic future. After work, I went straight home, ate dinner alone and usually fell asleep on the couch before 10:00 p.m. cuddled up with classic sitcom reruns. As long as this was my routine, I'd be single unless the mailman came looking for romance.

During that time, I went about my life without really thinking of the future. It was comforting to have a routine and be able to go through the day mindlessly. At night, it was different. My mind rummaged through the options while I mused. Struggling to fall asleep, I envisioned a forest, full of ugly trees and understood that my used saw was archaic by current standards. Longing to find the spot where fragrant pines grew wild, I tuned up my saw before setting out for the hills of Match, where I dreamed of finding a small grove to choose from.

The next morning, I awoke to the sound of a jackhammer breaking up the concrete sidewalk below. It was 5:00 a.m. and already noisy. This was New York City and true to form, it never slept. Tired from my restless night in the woods, I threw on a fuzzy bathrobe and ran downstairs to vent a spleen on the construction worker. When he smiled and shrugged his shoulders he said, "It's the only time the streets are empty lady." I knew he was right, but having awoken in a foul mood, I decided to give him the finger anyway before turning to leave.

Like the evenings, weekends were also lonely for me. At least from Monday through Friday, I kept busy, but on weekends, all I did was think about the fact that I wasn't doing anything. Up after my early morning trade, with the whole day ahead of me and nothing to do, I spruced up the apartment, fluffing pillows and changing the sheets. After breakfast, I decided to see if there were any last-minute cancelations for the 7:00 a.m. yoga class. Surprisingly, there were two. I dressed and rushed off to the gym to claim my place. I'd finally gotten a spot in the Zen master's class after being waitlisted for almost a month. If I rushed, I could get there before it was scheduled to start in less than a half hour.

Per the receptionist's suggestion, I wore yoga pants this time, albeit from TJ Maxx. When I walked into the gym, she smiled, nodding her approval. The regular crew of old men waved their welcomes as I walked past them into the yoga studio. Before even unrolling my mat, from across the room the instructor motioned for me to remove my shoes and without looking at me again said, "No shoes in my studio." Raj looked exactly as I would have expected a yoga teacher to. The smell of frankincense seemed to permeate every article of clothing on his tall, lanky body. I'd heard chatter in the locker room about him being so Spartan in his discipline, that nothing could rattle him. Raj was handsome in an intense, East Indian kind of way, with dark skin and pronounced facial features. His jutting cheekbones made it look as though he hadn't eaten in a week and I wondered how painful it would be to have sex with him and his protruding bones. Without any in the critical areas, I surmised it would probably be fine. His class was so popular, especially with women, that it always required a reservation. All the others in the crowded room were regulars who had carefully marked out their territory using blocks, mats, and blankets to create a line of demarcation to separate themselves from the common folk. Ah, the incomparable joy of getting stressed this early in the morning because there was not an empty space to park your yoga mat!

I was the only beginner in class. He guided me to the front where he could easily correct my posture. I laid my mat where he instructed, gathered my hair into a loosely tied bun just like his, sucked in my gut and was ready to start. The practice began slowly with soft chanting and music in the background. It was truly relaxing. His deep voice and slow rhythmic cadence were soothing in the same way that the sound of the ocean can be. The urban guru began by asking us to lay down face up on our mats. He directed each person to relax starting at the crown of her head and working down. Staying on each section of the body until the muscles visibly relaxed, it felt like he was the only other person in the studio. In a soothing voice, he told us that yoga released toxins and stress while he led us through a visualization that was an offbeat and eclectic mix of nice and not so nice images. My stress dissipated. I was truly calm and had settled in comfortably, focused on the class ahead. It was as though all the tension in my body had evaporated into the warm air. As he guided us through several asanas, the teacher gently corrected my posture twice, instructing me quietly on the change. The next time we were prompted to assume the warrior position, he came by and whisper-screamed at me, "Third time now, square your hips and move your right leg further back."

"I can't."

"What do you mean you can't? There is no can't. Direct your muscles to move as instructed and they will obey. You must take ownership of your body and command it properly," he said as he moved my hips towards the front of the room, then forced my leg back by placing his knee in front of mine and applying pressure.

Now that my legs were splayed a little farther apart than was sustainable, he nodded and said, "That's it." I felt accomplished but wondered if I could remain this way until he turned his back. It didn't feel right, but I couldn't bring myself to question him or dare to move without the emperor's approval. I started to feel uncomfortable and heard some gurgling in my stomach, but rationalized it away without giving it any importance. My stomach attempted to warn me again, more loudly this time. Persistently, it reminded me that this was always the first sign that some trouble could be brewing. Playing teacher's pet, I didn't want to move now that I was in full-fledged warrior and decided to battle it out. Being uncomfortable was better than getting another tongue lashing from the consummate yogi. After finally getting it right, my stomach decided it had a mind of its own. It spoke to me in a tone that sounded like a bad garage band before warming up. It practiced with loud noises which bounced chaotically off the walls in the cavernous space. I knew what was coming, but by the time I realized, there was no way to stop it. Even if I ran, there wasn't enough time to leave the room. So, in the quiet of the peaceful studio, I farted loudly and in my nervousness, began to laugh. The sound had carried and seemed to have been magnified by the stillness.

Offended, the guru said loudly enough for all to hear, "Please leave." As he starting rolling up my mat from under me he continued, "You have disrespected my class and have disrupted the aura. There is no farting in yoga." He said it seriously not realizing how funny it sounded. Maybe this yogi had watched *A League of their Own* the night before or perhaps he didn't realize where the reference came from, but his out of place movie reference made me laugh even louder. When I saw that this hybrid of Yoda and Hanks was not kidding, I quickly rolled up the rest of my mat and left quietly. It was very unlike me but after you punctuate a demand with a fart, there isn't much else to say. My takeaway was there is only so much you should relax when you've eaten a king-sized, Homewrecker burrito for dinner the night before.

Humbled by my extradition, I went home to tackle my closets. It had always been my go-to activity when I needed to find structure in life and was so much easier to do properly than yoga. At least at home alone, I wouldn't have to answer to a relentlessly rigid instructor.

My weekend had been uneventful other than the embarrassing incident. Without doing much, it seemed I was back at work in no time. Though the office was not a convivial environment those days, it was better than being lonely for a solid two days. For the past six months, work had become increasingly difficult. The company I worked for sold handkerchiefs, the quintessential Christmas present for the uncle who you didn't know what to buy for. Our business was dying a slow, painful death because of the dramatic changes in the retail market. Besides, who used handkerchiefs anymore? The only people who might have, were in the apparel industry and had probably cried into their last one while watching once healthy businesses disintegrate. Many of our clients had closed their stores. The sad truth of it was that the romance of my industry was gone. The pantheons called department stores that had once been hallowed showplaces for designers had become dated artifacts, like something you'd expect to find in a time capsule. Retail was in the tank. It was clear that the apparel industry was rapidly devolving into something quite different than it had been. Millennials were less married to brands. That demographic was more enamored with experiences. They were the new "all about me" generation and didn't indulge in designer clothing as their guilty pleasure. These kidults were more apt to have an expensive organic meal at a farm to table restaurant after a day of playing with their techie toys, than they were to go shopping. Their lifestyle choices ensured that the brick and mortar stores would shrivel away rather than thrive.

Howard, our CEO, was looking to place blame on anyone other than himself for the down trending volume. The rocket scientist had decided to purchase a new inventory management system for our recently upgraded mainframe computer at the same time as moving our warehouse to the west coast. Not only was this an expensive undertaking, but he chose to do it all two months before Christmas. A narcissist, who would never admit to taking on too much at once, he pretended away our problems even after the entire system blew up. Then, in a desperate effort to appease the board by reducing overhead, he stopped using third-party warehouses. This overburdened our own distribution center so much, that we were not able to deliver the holiday orders. The fourth quarter represented about sixty percent of our annual business, so this holiday, we had screwed up all our deliveries and our customers along with them. Although several of us had forewarned our fearless leader that making multiple changes right before the holidays would pose problems, he thought that as long as he was at the helm, we could weather any storm. He was wrong and as usual, everyone else paid the price.

As a result of the added pressure, work had become a Chinese fire drill every day. The millennial support staff was leaving in droves. They went to dot-coms where the perks were great, the bar was open, and the opportunities plentiful. Generally speaking, that generation placed an immense value on the soft benefits at their workplace. A Happy Hour of IPA flights on Fridays was worth more than profit sharing to them. For the older crowd, myself included, the pay wasn't bad. We were more hesitant to make a change that would disrupt our lives. We grew up in the business and were as loyal to our company as our parents had been to theirs. Many of my contemporaries had multi-tiered expenses with kids in college, mortgages, and new car payments. Some had alimony as the cherry on top of their financial responsibilities sundae. Even with no debt, I was a one income household and couldn't take a chance on making a change. So, we each put up with it for our own reasons, feeling that as the seasoned professionals we were, we could survive unscathed. We didn't foresee that a lower tide would sink all ships.

The corporate culture had changed. As part of the new normal, each of us kept to the task at hand and we didn't discuss the issues. It had become a chore to work and everyone left promptly at the imaginary bell. For someone like me who had always loved my career, this was just another disappointment in the assembly line of professional life. By then a VP at Luster, though it was not the ideal environment, I was hesitant to give up the devil I knew. Loyalty was a big thing for me. Howard often reminded me that he had given me, then an unknown entity, the opportunity to learn the accessories business. He brainwashed me into thinking that my success was founded on his benevolence, without ever acknowledging that I gave him an average of 65 dedicated hours weekly as payment in kind. He felt my loyalty was owed to him, and though I thought that in time it would get better, it didn't.

Howard had started talking about retiring when the board demanded accountability. He implemented a transition plan by hiring a new CEO in training. "In training" was his special title addendum coined for the new whipping boy. Michael, a member of the MENSA society, was the prodigal son hired to fix it all.

The bromance was on. The new guy definitely had book smarts. He had raw intelligence, without common sense, people skills or experience. To succeed, he would have to be willing to take advice from his time-tested team. Michael was too proud to ask for, or accept, any input. Some would parrot that two skills out of the needed five wasn't bad, but let's get serious, you can't turn around a failing company without being a five-tool player. I'd heard it said that if the only tool you had was a hammer, everything looked like a nail. It was precisely this kind of one dimensional problem solving that crippled us.

When I heard Michael's name, I always thought of him as the boy genius because his intelligence was revered when we were introduced. It had become indelibly etched in my mind. One morning, Michael asked for an overview of the company's business along with a listing of pending projects. As always "Miss I'll please him with my superior intellect and fact-checking" whipped it up promptly in full detail.

"Just put it right there," he said pointing to a stack of disheveled paperwork at the corner of his desk.

"Can I walk you through it?" I asked.

"You can, but you may not," he answered smugly.

Great, so that's how it's gonna be, huh? "Ok then. If you have any questions, please don't hesitate to ask me."

"I won't need to. I'm certain your report will read like a children's book and be self-explanatory. I've been told you always do such a good job with that. Please close the door," he said with a saccharine sweet smile as he looked at me condescendingly.

"And don't let it hit your ass on your way out said the empty suit," I muttered under my breath. I didn't know if he heard me or not, and frankly, it made no difference. I was protected. Howard knew how much I had done for the company and he wouldn't let this newbie destroy my career. Michael and I sparred that whole week. He took every opportunity to show me he knew better and to play boss, while I set out to prove him wrong by outperforming his expectations.

I should have realized what was happening. Disregarding the warning signs along the road, I went through life thinking that everything would be okay. Needless to say, I was often sadly disappointed. Optimism hadn't worked out so well for me. Until recently, I had given people the benefit of the doubt and often felt taken advantage of. So, after the collapse of my marriage and the painful process of a difficult divorce, I poked holes into every scenario, sure that it was just another masked version of a letdown.

I brushed off my battle with Michael and left the office that evening prepared to fully enjoy my free time. It was Friday after all, and I had taken a personal day on Monday to make it a three-day weekend. With a fun date lined up, I was eager to be on my way.

Starbucks, Friday Night 9:00 p.m. Tony

Ah, Tony was gorgeous in that swarthy, be still my heart, Southern Italian way. With delicious bedroom eyes and lashes that looked three inches long, he was just my style. My date was a construction worker who had a five o'clock shadow by 10:00 a.m. and looked like Pacino in his simply perfect Serpico stage.

When I got there, I immediately caught a glimpse of Tony seated in a booth. He was as handsome as in his pictures and smiling broadly. His coffee was already on the table and he warmly clasped my hand with both of his. I liked that.

"Hey Julie, I've been looking forward to meeting you all week. I'm beat. Would you mind getting your own coffee?" he asked slipping a twenty-dollar bill into my hand. "And maybe also get some sconce for us to share."

It was disappointing that he did not have the manners I expected on a first date. I was a little taken aback, but he did work in construction. Maybe I shouldn't have been surprised that he was a little less polished than I hoped for. Ok, I admit to have given credence to the stereotype about crass construction workers, but if the boot fits…

Who cared if he was not the perfect gentleman? He was hot and that earned him ample leeway. Besides, manners in bed were over-rated. They certainly were not what got him the four-star rating. I had singled him out because he could have been the Wikipedia image for sexy. Disregarding my initial impulse, I put on my big girl panties and went

49

for my own beverage. Isaac looked at me quizzically, but surprisingly didn't make a comment. I waited for my coffee, got a couple of sconce and started walking back to the table in the sexiest way possible. Then, true to form, while still within earshot of him, Isaac said, "Julie, it won't matter how hard you work it. Just walk and you'll have the upper hand."

What an asshole! Why would he ever say something like that? Approaching the table, I hoped Tony had not heard and saw he was looking at me appreciatively. This was a guy who clearly loved women. When I sat down and looked at him more closely, he was even hotter still.

Tony was the prototypical bad boy. He was the kind of guy I had always been a sucker for, with those expressive eyes that were deep soulful pools of brown lust – yum! From the nose up, he was someone I wanted to drag into the bedroom, but his smile betrayed him. Tony had a beautiful one that was infectious. When smiling, he looked like the boy next door, dimples and all. If you only saw that, you would have taken him home to meet your father because you could sense that he was dependable. Your mom, however, would have known immediately what the attraction was. She would have patted you on your backside and given you a doggie bag of vitamins to build up your stamina before you left.

As soon as I sat down, he spoke.

"So, I want to be honest."

"I knew it. It had to be something. You're going to tell me you are married, right?"

"No. I..."

"Have aids?"

"Julie, slow down. I'm..."

"Tell me you aren't a transsexual. Jeez, I can't wait to hear this."

"I will, if you let me speak. This is tough enough without you interrupting. I'm handicapped."

"Yeah, me too in many ways," I giggled.

"No, really. I lost the use of my legs in a construction accident about four years ago."

A long uncomfortable silence followed. I remembered his profile and thought he was kidding. "But one of your pictures shows you skiing."

"I apologize. I slipped an older picture in so I wouldn't send up any red flags," he replied looking downward.

"Oh my God, I'm so sorry."

"I didn't tell you beforehand because I wanted to meet you first and spend the evening in the company of a lovely woman. I thought it would give us the opportunity to share some stories, enjoy intelligent conversation, have some laughs, and see where it might take us."

"I can't believe it. I don't know what to say."

"No need to say anything. It's out of the way now. Let's just talk and have a nice time," he said smiling.

In his mind, it was out of the way but from the moment he threw his verbal grenade, it was all I could think about. I was consumed by questions.

My mind had taken me from a lusty bedroom scene to cradling him in my arms with pity.

"How did you get here?"

"My valet drove me, but only because I was running late. I'm really quite capable," he said trying to convince me. "My wheelchair is in the back. I didn't want to draw more attention to myself than was necessary. My upper body is strong enough that I can get myself into and out of the chair, but I need to be helped into the car and shower."

It sounded as if he had given this explanation a thousand times before.

"Please don't feel obligated to tell me more."

"Julie, you need to understand my capabilities fully. Please let me go on."

I nodded and out of the corner of my eye, saw Isaac intently watching the scene unfold. I shot him a dirty look and then focused my attention on Tony.

"I can have sex and often do with escorts. Don't worry, I get tested for aids every month and I'm as clean as a whistle."

"You don't need to give me an explanation."

"Yes, I do. I'm sure you are curious. At least I would be, so I want to answer any questions you may have, but first, let me say a few things. I work my construction business from home and employ six men who do the actual work. Financially, I am very comfortable. My house has been made completely accessible and if you decide that you want to start a relationship, I would forego the extracurricular activities."

"I don't know what to say. I'm at a disadvantage here."

"Listen, if this is not for you, I understand completely."

"You seem like a really nice guy. Maybe we can be friends."

"I don't need another friend. I have friends. I need to get laid."

"But I thought -"

"And not pay for it. I have a lot to offer the right woman and want to be in a committed relationship. I'm tired of being alone and phoning someone to pop over for a booty call. I don't think it is too much to ask for some genuine emotion sprinkled in between orgasms for good measure," he smiled warming up to the thought.

"What on earth do you look so happy about?"

"I'm alive. Spring is almost around the corner. I'm enjoying the company of an attractive woman, and I love coffee. If you give me a chance Julie, I promise you won't be disappointed."

It became apparent to me in an instant that I was a spoiled, self-consumed asshole. Tony was putting his heart and desires on the table for me to inspect, and all I could think about was his handicap. He was attractive and honest. The guy wanted a loving relationship and was trustworthy, I was sure of it. He even seemed to have a good sense of humor. Despite his handicap, he wasn't angry or desperate. I couldn't imagine how difficult it must have been for him to keep trying to make the best first impression and knowing that almost surely, he would face being rejected again. By the way he addressed it, I could tell he knew the soliloquy by rote. It saddened me that women had not seen past the chair to accept him for who he was. I expected better from them, thinking at least one would have looked more deeply to appreciate his candor and spirit. A great woman should have been able to open up her heart to this man. After all, everyone had some type of obstacle to overcome. There had to be a woman of enough substance in this world to see him for who he was, but I knew it wasn't me.

We drank our coffees quickly disregarding the huge, unspoken impediment. Trying to underplay it, we chatted about superficial things like how beautiful the day was and how caffeine was as good as a shot of adrenaline for energy. I was so uncomfortable both with the small talk and the energy it took to circumvent the obvious roadblock, that I scalded my mouth trying to gulp the coffee down as quickly as possible. He was bright and funny, and though the conversation was good, all I wanted to do was run away. I forced myself to be attentive and when it was time to leave, offered to wheel him back to his building. He lived only a couple of blocks away.

Tony replied that I could walk beside him if I wanted. "I have a handicap, Julie, but I am not an invalid. I am almost self-sufficient," he said.

I was in awe of his independence and of his determination to persevere in spite of his handicap. Though his efforts were admirable, I simply couldn't get past the chair. Without discussing the relationship offer again, we made light conversation until we arrived at his building. Tony lived in one of the stately hi-rise buildings that lined Central Park West. His doorman greeted him saying, "Evening sir," and sharing a warm smile. When he realized we were together, he turned away as though he was trying to offer us some privacy. I turned to face him and say goodbye. As I did, Tony said, "I'd like to see you again."

I couldn't answer him and looked at the pavement instead.

"You don't have to say anything else. I understand."

"But I'd love to be your friend."

Without responding, he rolled his wheelchair towards the lobby. Tony waved goodbye without turning to face me and the doorman dropped his gaze after opening the door for my date. It was as though I had rejected them both.

"Another one bites the dust," I heard Tony say before the entry door closed.

The doorman looked at me, disappointed with my decision, and turned his back to me as well. I couldn't hold back the tears. Feeling as though I owed them both an explanation, but not liking what I would have had to admit, I left instead. A relationship with Tony would have been impossible for me. I was angry with myself and should have been better than that. Sure, I could have soft pedaled it by saying that it would not have been fair to pretend considering a relationship with him. It would have been worse to give him hope, only to hurt him more down the road. I rationalized that pity was never a good starting point and it would have been a terrible foundation for a relationship. We were wrong for each other. I wanted more out of life and he deserved more from a partner. Though I was filled with remorse and saddened by my own prejudice, it was just too much for me to handle.

When I got to my apartment, I poured myself a double Maker's Mark and Diet Coke, my cocktail of choice when life had used me as a punching bag. The evening had pummeled me. As I sat drinking, I thought about what had transpired. I met a lovely man and couldn't see past his handicap. Did that make me a monster? Of course not. Sure, some life lessons were tough, but this one had crept up on me without my realizing it. Unsuspectingly, it forced me to look at my own shortcomings as well as his. I had looked forward to meeting Tony but the date turned out to be a major letdown. Even though he was really good company, I couldn't bring myself to consider him as a potential partner. I had always thought of myself as being open-minded, but this evening, the truth had been revealed to me. As Lisa always claimed, I was a black and white person. I continually fought the verdict, replying that fair and non-judgmental was a more accurate description. That night, I understood she was right. Tony had proved it without a doubt. There had never been a gray in my crayon box. For the first time, in this insurmountable frontier of my prejudice, I saw it. My mind was a steel trap. I couldn't budge it past the wheelchair. I tried to justify my reaction to his handicap by thinking it might have been different had I known in advance. I wanted to believe that in this case, a clear rejection had been the kindest outcome and tried to convince myself that I had given him a fair chance. Truth be told, I hadn't. I had been incapable of looking at him for who he really was, and for that, I didn't really like myself.

Tony- Construction Worker

The following week passed uneventfully with only two minor skirmishes with Michael, one over payroll and the other over advertising. The man thought himself a marketing guru and had implied several times that he understood women and what would motivate them to make a purchase more than I did.

Several weeks before, he had said authoritatively, "If I show a handsome man in the ad, women will want to buy these hankies to make them feel sexy."

I fired back, "Wrong. Men will buy themselves the handkerchiefs when they have a cold, and women will return them without opening the packages, because washing a snot rag is gross. The last thing a woman wants to do after she gets home and takes off her heels is to run a load of mucous through the washing machine. Our ads should romance a woman's mind by showing her exactly what hankies were meant to do - which is blindfold them!"

My secretary Aimee had stood and clapped. Madeline, who had not made it as a model and was hired permanently to be a member of my team shouted, "Woohoo!" Then three other women followed her lead. I hadn't realized that the disagreement had escalated and turned loud, but could see Michael was fuming because of the support the team had given me. It was at that moment that the relationship went from bad to insufferable. Needless to say, we went with his ad because he had the final say.

Several weeks after our argument, we hadn't even seen a slight uptick in sales from the expensive ad he had run in the New York Times. During our monthly meeting on advertising and social media, we evaluated the non-existent lift in business resulting from the ad. I smiled smugly at Michael's failure. For me, it wasn't about business anymore. It was all about proving him wrong. Reading my expression correctly, the genius stood up and dropped his notebook loudly on the table for dramatic effect, then marched straight into Howard's office, pouting like a little boy.

Howard had become increasingly irate as the numbers continued to slip. Though patience had never been a strong suit for him, he was now even more intolerant, if that was possible, of any projects that didn't show immediate results. The lack of revenue had made our already tense office environment more stressful than it had ever been. Michael's arrogance fostered a culture where it was harder to be creative and work as a team. By constantly pointing fingers to lay blame, he pitted us against each other making it difficult to work collaboratively. The team started to fall apart. Employees left eagerly, one by one to pursue other opportunities. Ever since Michael had joined Luster, Fridays couldn't come fast enough and each week seemed like it lasted a month. I counted the minutes until Friday like they were gumdrops, hungry to get my sweet 5:00 p.m. furlough.

That night, I was craving the anticipated break even more than usual. I was having coffee with a guy who sounded really friendly and dare I say it, normal. My date, Frank, was a NYC Cop who posted only a picture of his dachshund on his profile, but described himself as being 6' 3" with green eyes and dark wavy hair. He said he was 55 and had recently retired from the department. Frank was just starting his second career as a private investigator and I was eager to meet him to determine whether or not he would be the answer to my Missing Partner Alert.

Starbucks, Friday Night 6:00 p.m. Frank

A tall, handsome, café au lait colored guy walked in with a dachshund in a duffel bag to help identify him. When our eyes met, he smiled walking towards me and said, "Julie, it's nice to meet you. I'm Ralph."

"Where's Frank?"

"Frank is in the bag. I've done this for long enough that I've seen people post 20 year old pictures of themselves, describe who they'd like to be instead of who they are, and just lie a lot in general. I have learned to keep as much info to myself as possible."

"Got it. Not a bad idea. Thanks for the tip," I said.

"Stick with me kid and I'll show you the ropes."

I liked him and found our conversation to be effortless. The company was enjoyable, so we each got a second cup and continued talking. I needed a mentor in the dating trade and Ralph seemed to be an expert.

"How do you cull through the clutter?" I asked.

"You don't. It's a numbers game. Throw as much as you can against the wall and something's bound to stick," he replied.

I smiled remembering the potential sticky ones.

We talked about books, movies, and compared notes on our favorite pizza joints in the city. Both of us liked the same kind of films and confessed to being introverts at heart. Commiserating over the awkwardness of blind dates, our comfort zone with one another expanded quickly as did the topics covered during our exchange.

"I always feel like a third sleeve when I walk into a party alone. I never know quite where to put myself," I confessed.

Ralph laughed and said, "That's a great analogy."

When I looked at my watch, it was already after 8:00 p.m.

Ralph was a nice man but neither of us felt any sparks and by mutual accord, we decided to stay friends. We arranged to catch up with each other later that month and maybe see a film together. Ralph seemed like a decent guy but there was no chemistry. However, Frank won my heart in about two minutes flat. I saw myself reflected in his dark, sad eyes and fell instantly in love.

~~Ralph: Cop,~~ Frank: Dachshund *** keeper

Other than my fun date with Frank, the weekend had been routine so far. My not-so-glamorous New York lifestyle included two days of doing laundry, grocery shopping, going to the bookstore, streaming a movie and working out at the gym. Although my routine was solitary, in New York, you were never alone. Regardless of how early it was, even on weekends, there were lots of folks on the street. How could I be lonely? Wherever I went, I found myself surrounded by people, but felt isolated in spite of it.

That particular Sunday morning, yoga was packed and despite the fact that I hated crowds, it was nice to feel part of something. The class was more crowded than usual since the Zen master was subbing for Luciana who was sick. I would have known he was subbing even if I hadn't seen him. Upon opening the studio door, the smell of expensive perfume floated in the air like an echoed melody. Women prepped for his class by wearing makeup, fragrance, and jewelry - Om. So much for the simple yogi lifestyle.

Raj, my least favorite instructor for obvious reasons, saw me as soon as I arrived and watched me like a hawk eyeing its victim, ready to pounce at the slightest sound. I approached him, feeling very self-conscious, to dispel any fear of special sound effects during the practice. When we were facing each other I said, "No need to worry, no beans last night." He cracked a smile and added, "Thank you. Greatly appreciated. Namaste."

"Place your mat up front close to mine so I can see how you are doing," he winked. "Do I have your permission to correct your posture?" he asked. His voice rose at the end of the sentence, indicating a question without waiting for a response.

I knew enough to nod yes while smiling weakly, but he returned my hesitant smile with a broad, happy one of his own. People reacted differently once you exposed your vulnerability. They connected more easily with you when they had the upper hand, and as a result, they became much more approachable. The class had thankfully been uneventful and it turned out to be a wonderful way to start the day, especially since I was able to complete it emission-free.

CHAPTER 4

RUTH

After the gym, I went to Starbucks solo for the first time in a couple of months. In a good way, it felt sort of strange to be there and not be waiting for someone. I was in great spirits. It was refreshing not being burdened with having to pretend for a change. Lisa had recently given me a three week course on being myself, which just to be completely transparent, I failed. I didn't know how to be me when meeting a guy for the first time and was working on it by practicing being friendlier and more open with everyone. I approached the counter and greeted Isaac, "Morning. How are you on this beautiful day?"

"Better for your asking," he replied in a patronizing manner, addressing the next patron without having to ask me what I wanted. "Yes, ma'am. What can I get you?"

"Ma'am was my mother sweetheart. I'm Ruth and you skipped the lovely young woman ahead of me."

"I didn't skip her. I know what she's having. She's a serial dater who makes our little coffee spot home base. She'll probably meet some guy here in about ten minutes."

I chuckled under my breath at the exchange. Isaac was curt as always. The woman on the other hand, was feisty and self-assured. When I turned around to face her, I was awestruck. She was older, but extremely attractive, and looked as though she wasn't even trying. Radiating an understated elegance and inner beauty, her thick silver hair was cut in a shoulder length bob which looked so sophisticated that for a minute, I considered not dying mine. Nope, I wasn't ready for that yet. It was considered a gutsy move for any woman to allow her hair to go gray, but she wore it really well. When men grayed, they were thought to look distinguished, but it wasn't so for women. This lady did what few women could. She pulled it off stylishly. It was obvious she was confident and I found myself staring at her, hoping it was contagious. When she caught my eye, I smiled, and the gesture was returned with a nod and a smile that reached even her eyes and made them twinkle.

The woman looked at me and said, "It is a lovely morning, isn't it?" Her voice was as clear and crisp as the sound of good stemware clinked together in a toast. "I'd ask you to join me if I didn't already know you have a date. People should never drink coffee alone. For me, it is compulsory that it be accompanied by stimulating conversation."

"Isaac jumped the gun. I usually meet my Match dates here, but I'm alone today. Please join me, I'd welcome the company."

She reached for my hand and shaking it with conviction said, "I'm Ruth. So good to meet you."

Our conversation flowed effortlessly. Though not the norm for me, I found myself opening up and telling her about my difficulties at work. She listened intently and asked the type of questions that you wouldn't expect from a person you had just met. Ruth questioned why the relationship had become so adversarial with Michael. I had to give it some thought before answering.

"Because he is arrogant and thinks he knows everything. He never gives consideration to my opinions. I find him truly infuriating."

"With that kind of person, your job is to make him believe he came up with the ideas himself. That way, he'll be more open to them."

"That's brilliant, but it's gone too far for that. We hate each other and are battling our version of a professional cold war."

"How can you hate someone you don't even know as a person outside of work? Maybe he is just trying to assert himself and doesn't know how to do it. If book smarts are all he's got, the poor man has been burdened with feeling socially inept his whole life. You've got it easy. You only have to deal with his insecurities during business hours."

Our conversation went from work, to art, and then to travel. I found Ruth to be equally engaging on every topic discussed. My newfound friend had varied interests and a wealth of knowledge. It was evident that she was well-traveled. I sensed in her an ability to read most situations easily and intuitively to react in precisely the right way.

Having learned a great deal during our first conversation just by listening to her, I wanted to get to know her better. We had lots in common. It was as though we had known each other for ages when we spoke. This woman was compelling and seemed to be genuine. Now, why on God's green earth couldn't I find a man like her?

Ruth was a self-proclaimed film buff and just like me, loved independent films as well as the classics. We talked about our favorites, then about how much the movies being produced nowadays had changed. Neither of us enjoyed the meaningless, over the top, too much of everything films, which were favored by many as evidenced by massive box office draws.

"I can't understand why the movies now have so much going on with special effects. They are all about violence, nudity and foul language. What ever happened to the wonderful slice of life films that were so powerfully inspirational?" she asked rhetorically.

I answered anyway. "I think the industry uses special effects to make up for the content that is missing, like a shy woman might show a lot of cleavage to distract from her social awkwardness. Besides, people today want action and expect films to deliver excitement instantly. We've gotten so used to getting a quick payoff that it is almost as though we've been trained to expect instant gratification in every aspect of life."

"How can people expect things to have value if they come so easily? A microwave cannot replace the flavor of a slow cooked stew."

I thought it a brilliant correlation and was impressed that she assigned such high value to working towards a goal. Her observation surprised me since she looked like one of those pampered "ladies who do lunch". Recognizing myself as a victim of the "I want it now syndrome", I didn't admit to rarely taking the time to work things through. For me, puzzles were a punishment, and the struggle to reach a desired outcome, consistently defeated me. When I shared my vision of expecting to meet my love over coffee, Ruth laughed, and replied that there weren't enough beans being grown in the whole of South America to achieve that.

She had a great sense of humor and our easy conversation was animated and friendly. I could tell she was also enjoying it when her cell phone rang. Excusing herself to take the call for just a moment, she answered, "Darling, I'm having coffee with a lovely young woman. Can I ring you back? Yes, sure. I'd love to. Count me in and I'll bring a friend." She ended the call quickly. "Forgive me for answering the phone, but that was one of my sons." Her eyes were brimming with pride.

We chatted through our second cup. Before parting, Ruth invited me to a roundtable at the Angelika Film Center the following weekend. I was glad the call resulted in having the opportunity to spend time together again. Her oldest son's childhood friend had directed his first film and given her a couple of passes to the premiere. We exchanged numbers and Ruth agreed to leave a ticket for me at the will call window before she ran off. It was not until a few minutes afterwards, that I noticed her shopping bag on the seat beside me. I rushed out and tried to find her on the street to return the bag. She was nowhere to be found. I called her cell but got no answer.

By late morning, with most of Sunday still ahead of me, I made my way towards Central Park. It was still chilly and the weather was perfect for a brisk walk. Around the perimeter of the park's west side, I spotted Tony's building in the distance and slowed down wondering if he would welcome my company. Frankly, I didn't have the courage to stop when memories of the evening flooded my mind. Tony had made it clear that my offer to be a friend was not what he wanted. My reaction to his handicap troubled me. It made me doubt whether or not I was a good person and rattled the little social confidence I possessed. Tony seemed to be confident despite his challenges. Why couldn't I be? I had always been self-assured in business but was still unable to translate that skill set to my personal life. Frustrated with the schism, I left the park and chose the more direct route home on the streets which framed it.

The West Side had always been my favorite part of New York City. It was hip, but never as cool as the village. It had class, but it wasn't stuffy like the east side. The neighborhood was eclectic, with Lincoln Center on one block, and a thrift shop on another. It was a mixed bag, just like me. This part of town was home to several museums, a great swath of Central Park, fabulous restaurants, and its share of intellectuals. It housed everything one could want in the span of twenty city blocks. I loved the fact that many old-fashioned mom and pop stores still thrived there. The inhabitants of this enclave appreciated all things unique. I adored that about it and found it promising, hoping that someday, my own one-of-a-kind find would be unearthed in the neighborhood.

When I got to my place, the apartment I'd been occupying since Alan and I split, felt almost sterile. It wasn't really a house and it would never feel like a home. At least, it was mine alone and there was something to be said for that. Still, I missed having someone there to greet me. It would have been wonderful to know that someone was eagerly awaiting my return and cared about my day. The isolation made coming back to an empty apartment difficult and just called more attention to the voids in my life. In addition to the loneliness I felt, the aseptic style I had adopted didn't foster a cozy feeling either. Since the divorce, my approach to decorating could have been described as Scandinavian. It was minimalist and lacked warmth. If a stranger had walked in, and didn't know it was a private residence, he might have felt it was a one-bedroom suite in a business hotel. The only thing missing would have been the bible in the nightstand. I had never really taken an interest in furnishing the place. It was just where I lived for now. There were no photographs displayed, probably because the only ones I had were either of Alan or very old ones from family vacations. None of them had been properly cared for and I imagined many had tattered edges and were now faded. Alan had kept the little art we owned, not because he loved it, but because it was valuable. We hadn't fought over our possessions. Eager to wrap things up quickly and be done with it, I gave him almost everything without an argument. At times, I still missed some of the pieces we had acquired while traveling, for their beauty and the memories they inspired. Since then however, I found it increasingly difficult to become attached to material things, or even people for that matter. Everything here was disposable in my eyes. In a fire, I wouldn't have to worry about gathering my prized possessions. I had none.

These days I had few friends. Many of the ones Alan and I had made over the years were now uncomfortable around me. Not being part of a couple had made me difficult to approach. They didn't know what bucket I fit into, and after a while, many stopped trying to figure it out. Sure, people tried to fix me up whenever they met a single man, but other than that, I was not generally included in their plans. Infrequently, I socialized with a group of business associates who were more like acquaintances than true friends. We enjoyed our time together, but I'd seen even the closest business friends drift away from one another when either left the company. Lisa, who was like a sister to me, had her own family and responsibilities. Not wanting to intrude on family time or become dependent on her for entertainment, I never initiated plans, preferring to wait for an invitation instead. Since I didn't like to do things by myself or want to become an imposition, I stayed home a lot.

After my pity party, I decided to power up my laptop thinking that it would distract me temporarily and help get me out of my funk. I read the news and shopped a little, but was determined not to go on Match that afternoon, knowing it would only make me feel worse.

Of course, like with everything else in life, it was only when you stopped looking for something that it appeared. Just when I was ready to throw in the bed sheets, I received an email from a Match subscriber which read:

Hi Pretty Lady - Did you go to Elmwood High School and graduate in '87? I think we know each other and if I'm right, you haven't changed a bit. Write me back, I need to know if it is you - Matthew

Hi, Matthew – I did go there, but I'm sorry, I can't place who you are. Please fill me in, Julie

I'm crushed, but I'll try to get over it. It's me, 'Matt' from 7th period English – Mrs. O'Hanlon's class. We went to a Billy Joel Concert with a group of friends in our junior year.

Sorry Matt. Thanks for jolting my memory. I remember the concert, but I'm still not sure who you are. How on earth did you know it was me? It's

*been thirty years and lots of water has passed
under my bridge.*

*Hi Julia - It's Matthew, not Matt. No one calls me
that anymore. I recognized you because you are
still as pretty as you were then, maybe even more
so without the braces. How could I forget that
smile? Let's get together and catch up. Dinner this
Thursday?*

*Hi Matthew: That would be nice, but I can't do
Thursday. How's Saturday? JuliE*

*OMG JuliE! I see you are still as subtle as ever.
Love how some things never change. I'm dying to
see you, but Saturday won't work, and after that,
I'm away on business for the next 2 months. How's
the Thursday right before Memorial Day?*

I thought you gotta be fucking kidding me, could he
seriously be that busy? But instead wrote:

That works. When and where?

*J - Rossini's on 38th St. at seven o'clock. It's a little
old school, but then again, so are we. Anyway, the
food is still great. My cell is 646 813 1937 in case
anything comes up. See you in a few short weeks.
I'll be counting the days. - M*

Sounds great, see you then!

Without much more than a few lines exchanged, it
felt intimate. I was J and he was M, like we owned
the letters. It piqued my interest that he recognized
me and seemed to know me fairly well, stirring my
curiosity. Maybe I was just having a middle-age
induced memory lapse. I looked him up on Match
and still didn't remember him after seeing his photo.
I excitedly put the date on my calendar with a little
heart drawn alongside his name. Thinking back on

those days, I realized it was something the girls in high school would have done. A reminder popped up on my calendar about a coffee date Wednesday. It brought me back to the present. While there, I added the film at the Angelika with Ruth to my book as well. I was glad to have several things on my agenda to look forward to that week. Without them, I would have started obsessing about my distant date with Matthew.

I remembered to call Ruth about her bag again and was able to reach her. She was relieved that I had found it and wanted to send a messenger because she needed the blouse that evening. It would have been such an unnecessary expense, that I offered to drop it off myself. Though Ruth didn't want to impose, she relented by saying that if I could, without it being too much trouble, it would be a great help. With nothing else to do, I agreed to take it right over, and decided to walk since it wasn't far.

As I left my building, a guy walking alongside a woman with a stroller smiled at me and asked, "So, how is life in the single lane going?"

He looked familiar but again, my memory failed me.

"Nate, from Uber," he said realizing I couldn't place him.

"My God, I'm shocked you recognized me. Do you always remember people you give lifts to?"

"I usually don't, but when you help someone make a getaway, it becomes memorable. This is Maureen, my wife, and our newest addition, Mery."

His wife was lovely and their daughter looked just like him. Her curly black hair and beaming smile were identical to his.

71

"We live just down the block," Nate replied "See, we are neighbors just like I said."

"Well then, howdy neighbor."

"Don't forget to call me next time you need a ride."

"I won't. Nice to see you again," I said continuing on my way.

Ruth's apartment was several blocks away. Her doorman knew to expect me and instructed me to take the elevator to the 40th floor. When I asked him which apartment was hers, he smiled and said the whole floor was. As I stood in front of the elevator waiting to ride up, its doors opened and a man rushed out bumping into me. He apologized and when he caught my eye, I held his gaze for a moment longer than I should have. It felt electric. The guy was handsome but, lots of men are. That wasn't it. I felt an electric energy pulse through me. Something indefinable drew me to him and made him uniquely attractive to me. It certainly wasn't a trait that could be called out in a profile. I couldn't say what it was about him that was out of the ordinary, but it caused my heartbeat to accelerate, and even if for only an instant, there was an immediate connection.

I took the elevator up and when the doors opened, Ruth was waiting for me in her magnificent foyer. She was arranging a large bouquet of white flowers on an intricately inlaid wooden table. Noticing that I was looking at them, she said, "One of my sons just dropped them off. Today's a tough day for me. It would have been my 50th anniversary had Noah still been alive. I'm attending a memorial service for him in a few minutes. I can't tell you how appreciative I am that you brought my blouse over." Like the perfect hostess, Ruth asked me to come in and sit down, but it was obvious that she was just being polite. She was in the middle of getting ready. I didn't want her to feel obligated to entertain me, so I lied about having plans and needing to rush home to get dressed as well.

Ruth seemed to have it all, including children who loved her and wealth. No wonder she was so confident. Who wouldn't be when they enjoyed a charmed and perfect life? True to form, I glossed over the details, wanting walk in someone else's footsteps, without acknowledging the challenges they faced. I had developed the ugly habit of resenting the happiness that others seemed to achieve effortlessly. I never thought about the fact that she had lost her husband or experienced the bittersweet feeling of remembering love and feeling the loss.

By Wednesday, Michael had made me wish I'd planned a drink date instead of one for coffee. He challenged every damned thing I said to the point that it felt like he was trying to make me resign. Twice that week he dressed me down publicly. Although humiliated, I didn't defend myself. When he attacked my team, I never had any qualms about going after him. When it came to me, well now, that was a different story. Had I addressed it the first time, he might have stopped. By not doing so, I set myself up as easy prey for continual verbal lashings.

I'd received several texts from Andrew, my Wednesday night date, but never actually spoke to him before we met. At least in texts, he seemed friendly and carefree. I thought we would have fun together and was looking forward to meeting him. He was a photographer who lived in Bucks County and came to NY at least twice a week for freelance projects. On his profile, he had only posted an artsy photograph of himself cocooned inside a racecar, wearing a helmet. I wouldn't know who I was looking for when we met and hoped he would be able to recognize me from my profile photo.

Starbucks, Wednesday Night 8:00 p.m. Andrew

I didn't know much about him, other than that Andrew enjoyed running, loved to cook, and liked kids but never had any. From texts alone he seemed sweet, but shy. Maybe that was why he had not posted a good picture of himself.

I walked in to find Isaac grinning as though he'd heard a hilarious joke that he was keeping all to himself. Approaching the counter, I asked him if he had something stronger than Arabica back there and told him I'd had a tough day. He replied laughing, "I do, but if I gave it to your date, I'd have to proof him." He nodded towards the back of the shop, indicating that my coffee date was at the corner table. All I saw was some really young guy in high tops and a bomber jacket smiling in my general direction. I walked back to the counter.

"Yep, that's him. He said you wouldn't know who you were looking for."

"Holy shit, what is he, like eighteen?"

"Nah, I'd say 23 if I had to guess, barely legal. You sure can pick'em Julie. From senior hour, to the Special Olympics, then on to babysitting and everything in between. Brace yourself and go for it you cougar. You gonna breastfeed him so I can put it on YouTube?"

I walked over to Andrew and said, "I'm sorry, but I'm old enough to be your mother:"

"You are, but I've had the biggest crush on you since you guys lived in Queens. I'm Andrew Pescatore from down the block – Marina's son."

"Fuck me," I whispered to myself or so I thought.

"Love to," he replied.

"Excuse me?" I asked, my brain not wanting to trust what my ears had just heard. Moving on quickly before giving my date a chance to reply, or admitting that I felt like the sexy librarian in a teenager's fantasy, I continued, "So Andrew, where do we go from here?"

"Wherever you'd like Mrs. S," he replied.

"Holy Fuck," I said to no one in particular.

"Okay," he said. "You want me to put on a priest's collar? Ha, that's off the charts funny! Nah, really Mrs. S, you should be flattered. After all these years, I still think of you when I whack off."

I felt like an extra in a smutty remake of The Graduate.

"Now there's some information that I'd be better off without. I'll see you in another twenty years Andy. Good luck and go find someone your own age."

"Come on, you don't have to be like that Mrs. S."

I didn't hear the end of his sentence as I stormed out rhythmically in sync to Isaac's hysterical laughter. I turned around to silence Isaac's cackle with an icy stare before leaving, and as if to enrage me even more, the bastard held up both his hands as though surrendering. Without so much as sitting down with him, Andrew made me feel dirty and old, and for the first time in years, I felt the need to go to confession. Forgive me father for I have sinned. I've corrupted the little elementary school boy from down the block twenty something years ago...

Andy wanted to bag me, an old broad, just so he could check it off his "To Do" list, but I was not ready to be done. Yuck, disgusting!

~~Andrew: Andy, really?????~~

Matthew and I texted each other every few days. He never called and texted me only during business hours. Whenever I texted him in the evenings, a response never came until the following day. Was it odd or was I being paranoid? Maybe he had never overcome his shyness. I could see how texting would allow someone like him to become more comfortable expressing his feelings. The banter between us was sexy and fun. He was clever and seemed bright. I was looking forward to meeting him. Matthew must have told me twenty times how impressed he was that I had achieved such success in my career. Without having seen me in almost thirty years, I couldn't see how that would have mattered to him. He seemed super inquisitive about whether or not my job was lucrative. Though he tried to disguise them, his questions were largely about money and the things it could buy. That should have been my first hint, but I guess at times, you only see the signs you want to see. His most recent text claimed he couldn't wait to see me again and I admitted to being excited as well.

In the interim, I looked forward to spending time with Ruth again and anticipated enjoying a thought-provoking conversation after the film on Saturday. I even read a little about the movie in advance of seeing it in order to appear insightful. The film was about aliens stealing body parts. I didn't really like sci-fi, but had committed to seeing it with her because I had so enjoyed her company. After the film, the roundtable with the actors and director answering the audience's questions would be a novel experience. I was eager to hear about their creative process and what inspired the film. It would make for an enjoyable evening, even though a romantic film, would have been just the thing, to make the night fit me as though it were custom made.

I was running a little late and rang Nate to see if he could give me a lift. He was at the drugstore picking up a refill for his baby. Mery had been sick for over a week and he apologized for not being able to drive me that evening. He wanted to stay home to help his wife care for her.

I understood and made my way to the M train in a flash. If all the stars aligned, I could still make it on time. I rode the subway for a few quick stops before it came to a sudden stop. After several minutes, an announcement over the PA system said there had been an accident and our train was being held. The MTA apologized for any inconvenience the delay caused. Great! Ruth was probably settled in with her popcorn thinking I had forgotten about our plans, while I was stuck underground missing a fun night because of the infamous New York subway system.

Just as I was silently ranting my selfish tirade, the door which led from one car to another slid open, and a cop came into our car. He explained that a man had been on the track and was struck by our train. It appeared to be a suicide, but the police department had to investigate the scene prior to allowing the train to move.

Surprisingly, it wasn't the subway after all. It was just some faceless nut job that had put us all out. Why couldn't he have done the right thing, which in my mind was to run a warm bath, with a bottle of Vicodin, and a liter of Russian Vodka in the privacy of his single room occupancy apartment? I couldn't believe how self-centered that SOB had been. Cursing him silently for not having given any thought to the inconvenience his actions created for everyone else, I seethed.

A priest stood up in our car and started to say a prayer, then changed his mind. Instead, he spoke to his train congregation extemporaneously.

"Can you imagine the overwhelming feeling of despair this person must have felt in order to take his own life? The horrific feeling of loneliness must have been overwhelming. This troubled soul did not realize that while on this earth, we are never alone."

I mumbled that it was a crock of shit and the only thing we should be praying for was a speedy investigation.

"I'm not talking about God. Forget my collar. I'm referring to community. We are all part of something larger. Together, we create a quilt of humanity that engenders the spirit of a city. You may have heard some people refer to the pulse of the city. If it were not alive, would it have a pulse? So long as you are on this earth, you are never alone. Reach out to another human being when you see they are in pain and do what you can to comfort them. By giving love, you will receive it in return. In a large city, it is easy to lose your way.

Make it a point to find your humanity again. It will make your life heaven on earth."

It surprised me that he was starting to make a little sense.

"In a city where millions of people are rushing from one place to another, it is rare to find empathy without really looking for it. You'll find that when you look upon others with kindness, it will be given back to you tenfold. Give up your seat for someone who looks tired, donate what you can when someone asks for assistance, and reach out to help whomever you can. The person sleeping in a refrigerator box on the street was once whole. We don't know what life did to him to make him leave society. Bring him back and embrace his humanity. I ask you this from my heart, in the name of the Lord. Please give more so that you can receive unbounded rewards."

His words touched me. Maybe the aloofness that people who didn't know me well perceived, was a front to keep them from getting too close to hurt me. I knew that on certain occasions I put up a barrier, an invisible wall that kept others at a safe distance. The priest's words moved me, making me wonder if I ever really took down the façade. I did with Lisa at times, but never with others. The unconventional Sermon on the Train made me pause to think about my outlook on life and the face I showed the world. Did I allow others in, or even try to get to know people? The answer to both questions was no. I didn't dedicate the time needed to nurture relationships, but still expected solid friendships to develop organically. Good things take time, or to paraphrase Ruth, you can't microwave love or something like that. All it took was a death, a priest of some unknown denomination, and a group of selfish commuters like myself to call me out.

I couldn't pinpoint what it was about his sermon that I found so uplifting, his words or the sense of community they created. During my time sequestered on the train, I felt like I belonged to something bigger and it felt good. That was what I missed most about marriage, not Alan per se, but the communal "us".

While waiting in the subway, I thought about what the priest said and a gentle quiet came over me. The feeling was not faith. It was more mystical than that. I felt almost cocooned, like being swaddled in a blanket. The peaceful sensation was restorative and I found myself in a sphere of calmness. There, I wondered why I hardly smiled anymore. When forced to, my face contorted into a grimace. I hoped to find happiness one day, thinking it would be recognizable when I had it in hand, but in the meantime, I would have to keep looking. I prayed silently for the great number of things for which I was thankful - the use of my legs, crisp cold snowy days when all sound is deadened, my friends and family, flowers, pizza, quiet times, playoff baseball, my health, and finding a clean bathroom when one was needed. When I analyzed my life, the parts were all good, it is just that they didn't come together to form anything cohesive of value. The same thing had been true for the wish list that had become my profile. The all-important, indescribable glue was still missing from both.

After an hour, the train finally started moving again. Of course, since it was my life and I wanted to get somewhere, it backed up rather than going forward. My stop was the next one. It was so close, I could have almost reached it, if I stretched a little, until the subway started going in the reverse direction. The doors opened when the train arrived at the prior station and an announcement informed us that everyone had to get off. Before leaving, I approached the priest to express my gratitude. "Thank you, Father. Your words were life-changing."

"That is what I'm here for my child. Bless you."

I walked to the Angelika, got my ticket, and tried to be inconspicuous when entering the theater. Being almost two hours late, I knew the film would end soon. I could watch it in its entirety another time, but for now, my mission was to find Ruth in the dark, crowded theater. In the shadows it was difficult to pick her out from the crowd, so I sat in an empty seat in the back row. The credits rolled in less than twenty minutes. I had missed almost the whole thing and hadn't been able to follow the storyline or get to know the characters. As was accustomed only in LA, people stood and clapped afterwards to show their appreciation. It was only after the curtain dropped and the lights came back on, that my search for Ruth began. Not knowing if I would have enough time to locate her before the panel discussion started, I hesitated and lost my window of opportunity. The director took the stage. It wouldn't have been right to inconvenience people so I could sit down after the panel discussion had begun. Surprisingly, I stayed in my seat. Huh, maybe the priest's words had sparked a change in me. I thought of someone else first and though unfamiliar with that feeling, it felt good.

Surrounded by mostly older couples, I looked for Ruth but couldn't locate her. A woman with short black hair, that was stylishly cut, sat next to me. She was wearing a leather aviator jacket and smiled, greeting me. Deciding to evangelize, I extended my hand with the warmest smile I could muster and said, "Hi, I'm Julie. Hope I didn't create too much of a disturbance by coming in late."

"It is not a problem," she said in heavily accented English. "I'm Olga, very good to meet you."

"Likewise. How was the film?"

"I loved it. It make me remember when I first come to this country."

"The film was about Russian women?" I asked guessing at her nationality.

"No, it was about aliens."

Okay, I thought it a little strange, but fine. The woman sitting next to me identified with aliens. Don't judge Julia, breathe deeply, just live and let live.

"Since you are American, you don't miss anything," she said. I was somewhat offended for my entire country and wondered why she thought so little of our collective ability to grasp ideas.

The actors and director took the stage, and it surprised me that they looked like average people. I had always thought that sci-fi aficionados were geeky and lived in their costumes. After each spoke for a while, the panel turned to the audience for questions, and not one hand was raised. I felt uncomfortable for those on stage. Without knowing anything about the film other than what I had read, I asked the director why he had chosen extraterrestrials as the venue for his first film. He looked at me oddly without answering my thought-provoking inquiry and thanked me. Visibly uncomfortable, he moved on, trying to find another question quickly. When he barreled on as though he hadn't heard me, the woman seated next to me laughed heartily and said, "Even I understand it and my English was not so good."

Since no one else had questions, mine hung in the air, punctuating the silence as though demanding an answer. Rather quickly, the rattled director stood up signaling that the segment was over. I felt my phone vibrating and saw I had received several texts from Ruth to which I couldn't respond while on the train. Now, I had missed her call. Her message asked if I was still coming. Just before the call connected, my phone dimmed and the battery died. It reminded me of the suicide, and for the first time, I realized that too much had gotten in the way of my plans, an omen that the evening was not meant to be. I stood up to go home. After saying goodbye to Olga, I walked briskly to the train station. It had been a strange night. Despite the fact that I missed the film, I had been looking forward to spending time with Ruth even more and was disappointed our plans did not materialize.

As I descended the subway stairs, usually the quickest way to get anywhere in New York, two cops were cuffing a guy with his back to me. When they spun him around, I saw they were cuffing the priest who had so inspired me earlier that evening.

"There must be some mistake officers. This man lifted everyone's spirits earlier this evening after a tragedy."

"That's funny," the taller officer said. "He also just lifted three wallets and is not really a priest."

The faux Father shrugged his shoulders and gave me an apologetic smile. Regardless of his deception, his words had moved me and inspired me think about my demeanor towards others. Who he was hadn't really mattered. It had done me good to be part of his captive audience.

It's funny how the best life lessons sometimes come from the most unexpected places. I walked home thinking about what a strange night it had been. Once in my apartment, I charged my phone, changed into something more comfortable, and sat on the couch to open my mail over a bowl of Chunky Monkey ice cream. I never really got letters anymore and "the mail" had become a euphemism for opening up as usual, lots of bills. I followed each cocktail of debt with a spoonful of Ben & Jerry's, giving in to the fact that nothing can summons the carb cavalry as quickly as depression.

The phone rang, startling me out of my sugar-induced coma. It was Ruth. When I picked up, she sounded relieved and asked why I hadn't returned her calls or texts. I explained what had transpired and she immediately understood the ordeal it had been for me. Ruth was on her way home and suggested that I join her for a therapeutic cup of hot chocolate. After thinking about it for a moment, I agreed, not caring that I'd already changed into my knock-around clothes or consumed enough calories to light the Empire State Building for a week. We agreed to meet in half an hour.

When I got to Starbucks, Frank, the dachshund cop, was just leaving. We were both embarrassed that we hadn't gotten together as planned and he cut the tension by asking why I had come in my pajamas. I guess I did look a little out of place in patterned sweats and his levity helped us through the awkward chance meeting. We chatted for a few minutes before I saw Ruth walk in with a handsome, much younger guy. She found a table while her date, who was super-attractive, went to order. The crowd was boisterous on a Saturday night, different from that of the mornings or weekdays, and it surprised me how busy it still was. Frank stayed for a moment longer to chat, and again, we promised to stay in touch. Once he left, I walked towards Ruth and hugged her, apologizing for not having been able to meet her at the Angelika. She looked at me warmly, without passing judgment on how I was dressed. Her date approached, handing her a cookie and placing their drinks on the table. He looked familiar, maybe from the neighborhood or the gym. I guess there was a great deal I didn't know about Ruth yet. This handsome man only added to the intrigue and made me even more curious about her. They looked comfortable with each other and carried on as though they had been together their whole lives. She introduced him, "Julie, this is Luke. Luke, Julie." Her date admonished her affectionately and added, "Sure, I go get you a little something to have with your cocoa, and because I'm not back in 2 minutes flat, you give away my seat to the first beautiful woman who walks in. Seriously can't you stop being so charitable?" he asked smiling at her.

The questions multiplied in my head. Beautiful in sweats, really? Me? I was smitten but fought it. After all, he was with my friend.

Luke pulled up a chair and thankfully crashed our party. In the span of 10 minutes, Ruth had told me that he wanted to be closer to family and was moving back east from San Francisco. He confessed to never really enjoying the West Coast even though it was quite beautiful. The people were too nice and the pace too slow. A New Yorker through and through, he missed taxis, traffic, and New York bagels. I should have added that people always said it was the city water that made our bagels superior, but at the moment, all I could think about was him. Luke said New York was his home base and always would be no matter where he lived. I thought the city would be better with him in it.

Ruth smiled as he spoke. She was taken with his charm and reveled in his company. They had a warm relationship, which was friendly in a respectful way, and it was evident they connected on many levels. They even looked alike. People said that happened when you were part of a happy couple, but I wouldn't know about that. His eyes were intense, probing, and my heavens, oh so sleepy. Realizing I was staring and not wanting to be rude, I quickly shifted my gaze to Ruth. I noticed she was smiling and wondered if I had been caught. They continued their conversation without losing their way within the maze of words and sparred verbally for sport. No wonder they got along so well. They challenged each other's minds. Realizing that they hadn't been including me, Luke asked how my day had been. Too embarrassed to admit to feeling sorry for myself, I said, "It has been an unusual and eventful day. Unfortunately, my train was delayed and I missed an event I had been looking forward to attending."

"You see, this is not the kind of woman I'd ever meet online. She has a brain and interests other than landing a man," he teased Ruth. I cringed inside, thinking if he only knew, and hoped my embarrassment didn't show. "Look at how comfortable she is in her own skin. The women on those sites would never come out dressed as they are. They are never genuine. She is a natural."

Ha! He had noticed I was in sweats and didn't think less of me because of it. Instead, he saw it as a positive. This guy was really something. Maybe they weren't a couple. If they were, why would he speak so openly about other women in front of her? He seemed comfortable in doing so and it didn't appear to bother her either. I tried to figure out why they were so in sync with one another despite the obvious age difference and what looked like a very open relationship.

In response, Ruth replied, "In this high-tech society, Cupid takes many forms. You can't wait for a great woman to come to your doorstep asking you for directions to Target. Click away. Better living through technology, I say!"

I almost spat up my coffee because of my uncontrolled laughter, then discreetly tried to cover my guffaw. What a piece of work my newfound friend was. My mom used to say that age allowed you certain privileges, among them, the right to speak your mind without having to apologize for it. Apparently, this woman came from the same school of thought. Something kept drawing me to her date and I was embarrassed by it, but couldn't avoid it. My gaze drifted to him constantly. She smiled in my direction when she realized I was staring at Luke, almost nodding permission that it was okay to continue.

"I'm so sorry you missed the event. It was an interesting subject, directed with candor and compassion," Ruth commented.

"I would have liked to join you, but truthfully, I'm not terribly disappointed. I really don't care for movies about aliens or any other sci-fi."

"Oh, good heavens Julie, that belongs in the record books. You just can't make this stuff up. The movie was about illegal aliens my dear, not the other kind and you are the second person today to mix it up," said Ruth.

Boy, I was glad she didn't realize it was me, who asked the question from out in left field at the theater.

"It's a good thing you weren't there. My friend would have wanted the earth to open up and swallow him whole if he thought someone else didn't understand his film," Luke replied laughing.

Puzzled and looking at Ruth, I asked, "Luke is your son?"

"Yes, of course, hadn't I said that?" Ruth asked. "Who else would he be?

"At first, I thought he was your date," I said, and that's when Luke almost choked on his cookie.

Ever the detective, I put it all together and realized why he looked familiar. Luke was the man who almost ran me over in Ruth's building when I dropped off her bag. Now that I had settled the org chart in my mind and we each knew who the other was, it was all clear. In continuing our conversation, I learned that Luke was a commodities broker who had done well in New York, then moved out to San Francisco to be with a woman whom he later married. I could tell that Ruth didn't care for her when she added the color commentary that they married without really knowing each other. I didn't wish divorce on anyone, but was disappointed to hear he was married and wondered why his wife was not with him.

Isaac's minion, who was mopping the floor, turned to me and said, "My boss said that if you don't leave now, he will have to start charging you rent." It was only then that I noticed we were the last patrons still sitting. I looked at my watch and saw it was past closing and time for the evening to end.

"Too bad we didn't start earlier. I really enjoyed the company. It's a good thing he is kicking us out though. Otherwise I might have skipped my morning kickboxing class," I said standing up to leave. Out of the corner of my eye, I saw Isaac toasting me in the distance with a raised disposable coffee cup. He seemed to be acknowledging some imagined success. Ruth and Luke also stood now. Ruth hugged me and genuinely thanked me for a fun night. Luke agreed. They said how enjoyable it had been to get to know each other better and Ruth added that she was sorry I had missed the movie. She was impressive. This woman had to be in her late seventies, and although it was past eleven, she still had the energy I had not possessed since I was 40.

There was no harm in leaving the door slightly open since my invitation would be extended to both of them. "Perhaps we could do coffee again sometime."

Luke responded quickly, "I'd love that and will ask my mom to arrange it when I'm back on the East Coast. It is clear you two will become the best of friends. I hope to see you again soon."

As I walked out, trying to hide my smile, I muttered to myself, of course, she had to be his mother.

CHAPTER 5

MATTHEW

Although my dance card was far from full, work kept me so busy, that the time passed without my even being able to complain about it. Michael had gotten into the habit of shifting everything from his desk to mine, which in essence doubled my workload. Then, he had the audacity to critique almost every project my team collaborated on. I had come to learn that his occasional silence, meant only that he could not find fault with my work. I always braced for negative feedback and was pleasantly surprised when none came. Perhaps he and Isaac were related, or maybe they'd gone to the same finishing school and both flunked. I brushed these thoughts aside and prepared for the upcoming holiday weekend by organizing my desktop and compiling a to-do list for Tuesday. Memorial Day weekend was finally here for me. I'd taken Friday off as a vacation day in anticipation of a great date with Matthew.

I went home to change into the dinner outfit selected weeks ago. With one thing less to obsess over, I took a very long, hot shower. Time was always at a premium, so I relished the luxury of being able to dress, at something other than breakneck speed. Wanting to look like I wasn't trying, I took an inordinate amount of time getting ready. After finishing my makeup, I selected the perfect fragrance to channel my sultry side without being overbearing and got dressed. When I looked in the mirror, I felt pretty. The black flared skirt camouflaged my hips while accentuating my waistline. My new wraparound white silk blouse coupled with a lightly padded bra made it look like I had cleavage, and to top it all off, I was having a good hair day. Everything was working out according to plan.

I fished out Nate's card from the black hole that was my handbag, thinking that the casual conversation would be a good way to start my evening. To my surprise, he was already there when I walked outside five minutes early. My concern over whether he would be punctual or not, turned out to be wasted energy.

"Hey Julie. Thanks for calling. On long weekends, the city is usually a ghost town, so I welcome the business. Everyone seems to flee from Manhattan when they have extra time off."

"No problem. I would have already used you a couple of times if your card had not gone missing in my bag."

"That's the story of my life – used and abused! Figured you were married and living in suburbia by now when I hadn't heard from you. So, who is the lucky guy?"

I filled him in on Matthew. Nate listened attentively saying that if something was meant to be, it would be, even if it took a few decades. When I asked him if I looked okay, he turned around at a red light to check.

"You're a knockout, but you smell even better than you look. What perfume are you wearing?"

"My favorite – Must by Cartier."

"I've got to get some for Maureen. Ever since she became a mom, my wife claims to have forgotten how to be a woman, but if you ask me, she's sexier now than when we first met."

The drive took only about ten minutes and we talked the whole way. Nate did most of the talking, telling me about his wife and daughter.

"Maureen is the heavy hitter when it comes to salary. She's a big-wig at P&G and is just going back to work after four months maternity leave. It's been tough for her to even think about leaving the baby and now she is obsessing over hiring a live-in nanny. You can't imagine how much that costs in Manhattan. It will really help to have her salary back. I don't know how women without a salary at the high end of six digits even work after having kids."

"I know. My friend Lisa only went back to work after her daughters got older. Day care was so expensive that she did odd jobs from home for several years so they wouldn't have to pay it."

Pulling up to the curb, he said, "Well, it was good to catch up. Hope your date is great. After all, you've waited a lifetime for it. Put my number in your phone so you don't lose it in handbag hell next time. That'll be seven bucks, Julie and by the way, happy hunting."

I gave him a ten and told him to keep the change. As was always true with him, the ego boost was worth the extra three dollars.

When I walked into the restaurant, Matthew was sitting at the bar having a drink. He was very handsome, with a classic profile, and dark hair peppered with just the right amount of gray. Though he didn't look comfortable and was a bit overdressed in a suit and tie, I found it endearing

93

that he had dressed up for me. I wanted to step back to watch for a few minutes longer before approaching, but I was too eager to meet him. I couldn't temper it and gave up playing the game to walk inside. He seemed to be in his own world, fidgety, mumbling to himself, and oblivious to me. Ok, so what if he was just a touch crazy? That could surely be overlooked if the rest was good. Matthew had not looked up until I was close enough to touch him. When our eyes met, he stood and smiled, then handed me a single red rose and softly kissed my cheek.

"Hello again. You look well," he said. His voice was deep and silky smooth, like honey.

"You too," I replied flushing.

People changed, but even if you hadn't seen someone in years, there was usually a familiarity about them that would trigger a memory. His profile did it for me. I remembered him now. Matthew was the shy boy who wore glasses and sat two rows to my left in sophomore English class. He had never said more than a dozen words to me or to anyone else if memory served me. Seeing him, I remembered how nervous he often looked when the teacher called on him.

I had participated in multiple school activities and special interest clubs. Being active led to having lots of friends in high school and I remembered those days fondly as some of the happiest times in my life. Lisa always said that my perceived "Miss Most Likely to Succeed" sash made me intimidating to approach, but I never felt it did. Instead, I thought the spoken accolade probably made people want to get to know me better. Matthew had been the opposite, a brooding loner who never seemed comfortable in his own skin. We travelled in different circles and in those days, I never reached out to include him. Thinking back on it, maybe I should have. From the looks of it, in the thirty years since I'd seen him, he became the swan, and I the ugly duckling. I found myself hoping that along with his deepened voice, he'd grown up and become more confident too.

"Would you like a drink here or at our table?"

"At our table is fine. Thanks."

"Great then," he said as he placed his hand on the small of my back guiding me. It wasn't meant to be sensual, but I could feel the heat of his hand through my silk blouse, and something as casual as that sent a shiver down my spine. It had been a long time since I'd felt a man's touch and frankly, until now, I had not realized how much I missed it.

His manners were impeccable. He asked where I wanted to sit, with a view of the room or facing the pianist. I couldn't imagine who this guy had been dating to ask such a question. It was so over the top that it seemed disingenuous. I didn't care where my seat was as long as the food was good and the company better.

We sat across from one another. For a minute, neither of us knew what to say. Our uncomfortable silence was cut short when the waitress thankfully approached us, to introduce herself and to recite the daily specials. She could have easily been one of the hundreds of starving, out of work actresses waiting tables in New York and looked out of place in her uniform. Tall and svelte, she would have been more at home on a runway. One could have described her as pretty, but in a pinched kind of way, as though her face had been lifted one time too many.

"Oh," she said gushing at the rose. The 'oh' turned into a moan rather than a word and I wasn't sure if she was coming or going. "An anniversary?" she asked.

Before I could speak, Matthew replied, "Yes, actually it is. We've known each other for over 30 years and just found one another again. Isn't that romantic?" He actually batted his eyelashes as he spoke, morphing into a boy with a wide-eyed, innocent look. I had never even seen a woman do that. Seeing him pull it off, I understood how it could work, and made note for future reference. For some reason I missed, no decided to disregard, how scripted his dialogue was. It was almost memorized, but against my better judgment, I chose to ignore that.

Instead of my brain sending in the cavalry screaming "player, player, beware the empty suit," I let myself be swayed by the flower, by his manners, and by how hard it appeared he was trying. I should have run when I sensed he could be trouble. Instead, his actions drew me closer.

We ordered cocktails to have with our appetizers and asked her to come back for our meal order. He was quiet and I, in my nervousness chatted for several minutes about our class together and high school in general to fill the silence. When she returned with our drinks and calamari, she lingered waiting for us to order our entrées. Too young to have been touched up, our server was modeling more than waitressing, with her cheeks sucked in as though posing for a glamour shot. Upon closer examination, I saw her shoulder bones sticking out through the blouse and realized you could have blown her over with a sneeze. Her crack-addict couture image, coupled with how uncomfortable Matthew looked, made me expect Rod Serling to pop up from behind the partition to tell me that I'd been re-upped for a recurring role in The Twilight Zone.

After the initial silence, we enjoyed our meals with only a few breaks in the conversation. I can't remember what we spoke about, but do recall a pianist playing Sinatra classics in the distance. The music helped set the mood for a special night. With Frank in the background, we danced verbally rather than speaking. Matthew and I each played with the other's words, flirting and trying to impress one another with our wit and intelligence. It seemed to be working. He looked mature and acted like an adult, but for some reason, I couldn't help thinking that he was playing dress up in his daddy's clothes. Though it was obvious to me that both of us were on our best behavior, I couldn't figure out if he realized we were acting. He appeared to be so entrenched in the role, that it should have made me wary.

He became a little more at ease after a couple of cocktails, but other than when playing his part, Matthew never relaxed throughout our entire time together. Every time someone moved, his eyes followed them. It was weird and kind of creepy, like I was in a haunted house. Maybe he was just attentive or didn't like having his back to the door, so I asked him if that was what was making him skittish. He remarked how observant I was and said I had picked up on one of his many idiosyncrasies.

After reminiscing for some time, we spoke about our lives since then. I filled him in on what I'd done after high school, explaining that I had been married, but glossing over the details. Matthew had also been married and was much more willing to share his history. His wife had cheated on him and while it broke his heart, he was not bitter. They had no children, were still civil to each other and often saw one another at gatherings. His attitude towards her was casual and it seemed we were both ready to move on.

Matthew owned an outsourcing agency that hired workers for no more than 29 hours a week. "When human resources use our services, they save their corporations tons of money. They don't have to pay for health insurance since the workers are all part time employees," he gloated, pleased with his resourcefulness.

It sounded sketchy to me, but he said it was common practice and his business was thriving. Even if only for an instant, I wondered what kind of person made a living by cheating others out of what was rightfully due to them.

Once we got the synopses of our pasts out of the way, I learned Matthew liked to read and enjoyed the theater. A mere two hours had passed and I was already smitten, visualizing a future together. My emotions were too strong, too fast. I had to pinch myself to make sure I wasn't dreaming, but I never claimed to be unsusceptible to the fantasy, and was back in the moment soon enough, when the waitress interrupted my dream world to ask if we'd like anything else. Matthew informed her that we would be moving to the piano bar for dessert and coffee. Disappointedly, she asked what we wanted, and he ordered for us both. We walked to the bar. When the pianist saw Matthew, he acknowledged him. Matthew smiled in reply and walked over. He put a bill in the tip glass while whispering something to him, then swaggered back towards me, apparently pleased with himself. The waitress delivered our desserts and thanked him while letting her hand linger on his when she gave him the check. You know how some waitresses draw smiley faces on checks? Well, she had decided her phone number was more apropos. It was unbelievable. Even more outlandish than her brazen ploy to lure him in, was the fact that she was doing it on our anniversary!

Once she left, he took my hand when the pianist started playing "As Time Goes By". Though corny and gimmicky as hell, for me, it was just the right thing to make it a perfect night. I should have reminded myself why it was that I hated it when the music swelled in films. It always made me feel as though the director was trying to manipulate my feelings, and I despised being toyed with. I didn't see that my date was orchestrating our evening the very same way. We lingered over our coffees, enjoying the music, and when it was time to leave, Matthew drove me home. The date turned out to the kind that begs for another one to follow. I knew some of it was staged, but fell for it anyway.

By 11:00 p.m. Lisa had reached out three times with texts.

So…

So, it was perfect!

I've got a crazy day tomorrow. Ellie is going to the junior prom but I can't wait to hear all about it. Coffee tomorrow at Starbucks before the girls wake up?

Maybe.

See you at nine for a quick cup. I'm not taking no for an answer.

Yes sir, I mean ma'am. See you then!

I enjoyed a deep sleep that night. The romantic evening had worked its magic and I was enamored with the thought of saying "we".

I got to Starbucks just as Lisa was getting in line. She greeted me with a warm hug. Isaac was never hospitable, and true to form, he had a sarcastic remark stashed away in his back pocket waiting for the opportunity to see daylight. In anticipation of the thrill he would get from the jab, he moved the line more quickly than usual, while I readied myself for the nasty comment I sensed was coming. Isaac looked at Lisa and asked what she wanted. When he got to me, all he asked was whether I was switching teams. Having prepared for the blow, I responded that it beat meeting guys like him and trading down to new lows. My quick delivery reminded me of why one should always prepare.

When we sat down, Lisa said she couldn't stand him and asked if I was sure he hadn't poisoned my coffee. Getting over it, she continued, "Give me all the details, but quickly and without editorializing because I don't have much time."

I filled her in without skipping a single important detail. When she heard about the song, of course, an eye roll followed. Undeterred, I didn't even acknowledge seeing the gesture and continued telling my story. "Then, when we were about to say good night, he drew me in and before kissing me, asked me if I would like to see a show on Wednesday night. In my excitement, I told myself to go slow, but said it out loud by mistake. He heard "no" instead of "slow" and looked crushed that he was being turned down. It was so funny and sweet. I had to correct myself and say yes to the date." I smiled reliving the story through her, though she didn't seem as impressed with him.

"What an ass," she laughed.

"What do you mean? He was perfect."

"Perfectly scripted," she replied. "Sounds like he had it all figured out. Plus, if he's a regular there, you can bet he's done this before."

"It was great and we are going out again on Wednesday."

"You're acting like you haven't gotten any in forever. Get a hold of yourself and use your brain. You don't even know this guy."

I had to concentrate to think of anything other than him, but said, "Yes'm," as though taking a quick trip back to being punished in middle school for not doing my homework.

"Don't say you understand just to shut me up. If you don't slow down, you'll fuck it all up. You went on ONE date. Get serious and get to know him before you rent the reception hall. Besides, he sounds like a con artist who also happens to be a serial dater. I'm worried about you."

What if she was right? The instant I acknowledged my doubts, I should have listened and given Lisa the car keys. It was clear that I still needed a designated driver when it came to romance. My loneliness level exceeded the legal limit. All I wanted was to feel again. Nobody could blame me for that, right? My heart had been numb for a long time and now it was starting to tingle. Being infatuated was good for me. Besides, the endorphins had already kicked in, clearing the way for love.

I wanted to cancel my other dates but Lisa talked me out of it. The next one in my line-up was with Troy, the personal trainer, on Monday morning. She reminded me that his profile had shown only a picture of his pecs and that after seeing it, I said if he looked half as good as his chest did, he was a keeper. Troy and I had spoken a couple of times and learned we had lots in common before he asked me to lunch. After a bit more conversation, he invited me to work out beforehand. I thought it would be a fun thing to do together, however, things had changed since then. I swore to keep the date no matter what, but at that moment, I saw Troy only as a way to get fit for the upcoming Olympic floor exercises with Matthew.

On Sunday, Lisa and I had planned to have brunch and then go shopping for my gym date. I needed new workout clothes that didn't resemble what I really wore to exercise almost every day - still sweat pants and a tee. While we ate, Lisa showed me pictures of Ellie getting ready for the prom. She looked stunning and I couldn't remember ever having skin like hers. It looked as though she were made of porcelain without a pore in sight. Wistfully, Lisa said she still thought of Ellie as her baby and couldn't believe that she was already a beautiful young woman. Time had certainly passed, but you wouldn't know it from the way we acted. We behaved like giddy schoolgirls after two Bloody Marys apiece and were feeling pretty good by the time we went shopping. Thinking back, it might not have been the best idea. Just like you should never go grocery shopping when you are hungry, there should have been an ordinance against shopping after a boozy brunch. Store security should be required to perform a breathalyzer test at the register. I could have done a lot of damage to both my wallet and image by SWI - Shopping While Intoxicated.

We hit several stores before arriving at Century 21 on Broadway. Their activewear department took up almost the entire floor and was quite busy. Thirty-year-old women flitted past the fixtures knowing exactly what they were looking for. Lisa and I were at a loss and not only because of the vodka. To us, gym apparel was only to be worked out in, not to be worn as a mission statement on your lifestyle.

"Where are the legwarmers?" I giggled a little too loudly.

"The chick in the dancing movie bought the last pair 32 years ago," Lisa parried back. She showed me a pair of zebra striped leggings. I wasn't sure if she was kidding or not, and didn't want to hurt her feelings, so I moved on without responding. She cracked up and said, "Gotcha." She understood me without my having to explain myself and we always had fun together. We talked about everything from the news, to men, to dieting, then back to our favorite subject again, men. We had been friends for over three decades and shared volumes of history. Each knew the other well, and though our lives had taken very different paths, we still loved each other and had a blast every time we were together.

"We should have invited Ellie to shop with us. She would have known what to wear for a workout date," I said. We were both a little out of touch. I had not been interested enough to care and Lisa had been a stay-at-home mom. For many years, it had isolated her. Now that the girls were older, she had joined the workforce again part-time as a bookkeeper for a small accounting firm. "You know I can't believe how much I enjoy working again," she said.

"Give it time and you'll come to find out all over again that work sucks. At least you don't work for a vulture who keeps digging his talons into you every opportunity he gets."

"Don't let him get to you, Jules. He must be henpecked at home and asserting his authority the only place he can. Besides, he's making you his doormat only because you let him." I looked at her sullenly and then she added, "Hey, it's not too late to change that. Stand up for yourself or be resigned to let his bullshit roll off your shoulders. Disregard half of what he says, and the other half, write down for when you have to take him to court," she said jokingly.

"He's such an ass. He loves grandstanding in front of an audience. I hate that, but it's not what scares me. The most dangerous thing about the moron is that he has Howard's ear."

"Play nice. The guy is going to take over soon enough."

"How can I play nice when he's got it in for me," I asked.

"At least, give him a chance. Next time you meet with him alone, tell him that his support would mean a lot to you and convince him that you are a team player. Open up to him, share your business plans and present your ideas professionally. Try to make it work. If he doesn't value your experience or appreciate your ideas, then tell him to shove them up his ass."

"No, he might like that. It probably looks like a museum in there already," I guffawed and the girl across the fixture from us laughed mid-gulp and ended up splashing the workout wear with her Frappuccino monsoon.

"Great. Absolutely great," she said. "I can't wait until I'm old enough to say whatever I feel without caring how it sounds."

"Are we really that old?"

"I guess so, or at least she thinks we are," Lisa replied. We decided on an outfit quickly after that. Who cared what I looked like anyway, now that Ms. Designer Coffee 2011 had spelled it out for me so clearly? I was past the age when anything mattered, so why bother?

Even without Ellie's help, the outfit we selected for my date the next day was really cute. My athleisure purchase was fashionable and color coordinated.

94th St. YMCA, Memorial Day 10 a.m. Troy

I got to the Y on time and walked in trying to look as relaxed as possible in my new sneakers and just purchased workout gear. Striding towards me, as though he had been born on a treadmill, the face that went with the pecs was just what you would have expected. Troy was a smoldering hot, surfer boy. My fantasy incarnate was smiling broadly, apparently pleased with me as well. Kismet, I thought, warming up to the fact that after two years of nothing, now twice in one week, I felt the warm trickle of lust radiating down my back. Two hot dates in a week was a new record for me. It would have been a good week to invest in a lottery ticket, but I didn't want to jinx it by pushing my luck.

When he asked if I was ready to work hard, I answered, "Born ready!" Troy laughed and suggested we start with a 20-minute warm up on the elliptical. I found two machines side by side so we could chat and was surprised when he walked away from me. I lost sight of him and figured he'd gone to get a water, so I started the cardio workout slowly by myself. Troy returned and handed me a towel, then a bottle of water, but he didn't get on the machine beside me. I was puzzled and asked why he wasn't exercising. He laughed, apologizing for not explaining himself well. The date was to have a free workout session with him as my personal trainer, not to work out together. Surprised and somewhat disappointed, I said okay, certain that I'd only be going through the motions of a workout while we got to know each other. Boy, what a mistake! After the elliptical, Troy started my training session with some boot camp exercises. Stop watch in hand, he counted out three sets of twelve each before he would let me rest for a few seconds. Fifteen seconds to be exact. That wasn't enough time to even plead for mercy. From there, we went straight to the next exercise. When I thought we were done for the day, he said, "Not yet, you have another round cardio." He put me on a treadmill and once I got comfortable with the pace, he increased both the speed and the pitch of the machine. After 20 minutes of holding on for dear life, he stopped the treadmill and asked if I was okay. So out of breath that I couldn't speak, I nodded yes. He replied, "Great, then let's finish up with the circuit training machines."

Pushing me every step of the way, by the end of the 90-minute workout, I was completely drained, but tried not to show it. I replayed our initial conversation in my mind and realized that I might have grossly overstated my fitness level. I kind of remembered saying that I was training for a triathlon.

"So, how do you feel?" Troy asked.

"Great," I lied again.

"Are you still up for brunch?"

Shit yeah! I was starving but managed to hold my tongue. Instead I answered, "I'm never really hungry after a good workout. I'd be happy to join you though." What I really should have said was that I might not be able to muster up the energy to raise a fork.

"Let's take one car. I'll pick you up right in front of the gym," he said, erroneously assuming that I had driven.

"Do you mind if I freshen up?"

"Of course not, but don't be too long, I have reservations at Teachers Pub and if we are not on time, they won't hold our table."

"Great," I said rushing to the bathroom to fix my hair and wash my sweaty face. I was glad I wasn't trying as hard to impress this guy as I would have been before my date with Matthew. After freshening up, I walked out of the gym shooting for cool and nonplussed. Thinking I'd achieved it, with positive self-talk, I said, "I got this." Then my legs gave out from under me refusing to lie any longer. The bastard turncoats buckled and surrendered, forcing me to take a knee in the middle of the parking lot from the tiny effort of stepping off the curb.

"You okay?" Troy shouted out as he bolted from his car.

"Yeah, I'm good. I must have tripped."

"You didn't trip. You must be beat. I worked you over pretty good. I figured I'd teach you a lesson in honesty with a triathlete boot camp workout."

"Was it that obvious?" I asked knowing I had been caught.

"Are you kidding? Of course, it was."

"When did you first realize that I had stretched the truth?" I asked.

"The minute I saw you. No real athlete shows up to a workout wearing new kicks," Troy replied candidly. "Don't worry though. You are not the first and I'm certain you won't be the last. You were a really good sport."

More than a little embarrassed, we both laughed it off and went to brunch. He was driving a classic, mint condition, aquamarine blue Karmann Ghia with black leather interior that looked as though it had been made for him. It was actually the same color as his eyes.

"Nice wheels," I said. "How do you keep it in such great shape living in Manhattan?"

"I don't. This is actually a Luxe Rental. You're not the only one who spruced up for brunch today," he admitted.

After getting off to a bad start by pretending to be whom I wasn't, it was time to give up the act. Even though he was handsome, after the initial thrill, there was no chemistry between us, so being myself came a bit more easily. He was amused when I confessed to expecting a light workout with lots of talking and only a little exercise.

"I dished it out pretty hard. You'll be lucky if you are able to walk tomorrow. I just hope you won't hate me for it."

"If I don't already despise you after the torture chamber you put me through, you're safe."

When he dropped me off at the gym again, he said, "Thanks for a really nice time and for reminding me that if someone doesn't like you as you are, they can take a hike. Take care and good luck Julie."

"Yep, you too. Thanks," I said. "Oh, before I forget, give me your card in case I ever decide to step up my routine and really need a trainer." He kissed me on the cheek and gave me his card. The date had been good. It reminded me to be myself and also made me realize that it was time to step up my workouts.

Troy: The Trainer

CHAPTER 6

LAMENTATIONS

On Tuesday, it was back to work. I wanted to treat myself and went to Saks at lunchtime, to shop for a dress for my theater date with Matthew. It had always been my favorite store, but now with many people doing their shopping online, it felt like a mausoleum. I was there alone except for a handful of tourists. Wanting to look elegantly sexy and provocative, I was more selective about choosing the dress than ordinarily was my style. Finally finding one that fit all my criteria, I realized it was already half past noon. Our weekly marketing meeting was scheduled to start in thirty minutes and Michael had been known to lock people out if they arrived late.

By the time I left the store with my purchase, I had little time to walk the half mile in heavy pedestrian traffic. Normally, I would have run back, but even Michael couldn't fluster me this week. I was infused with energy. In my mind, life held nothing but promise. With a spring in my slightly sore step, I made it back to the office with three minutes to spare. Michael looked disappointed to see me. When I asked him what was wrong, he curtly replied that it was nothing. Of course, I couldn't leave it at that.

"Are you disappointed that you won't get the opportunity to lock me out?" I asked. He replied that yes, frankly he was. I smiled, surprised by his admission and added, "Don't you worry. You'll get another chance for sure."

I thought it odd that Matthew hadn't reached out between dates. Not even a text or call until the day before to confirm. Even then, it was just the needed details in an "If I tell you, I'll have to kill you" spy-type communication. Matt, I mean Matthew, texted me that he had gotten tickets to see August Osage County. It had won every award imaginable and was highly acclaimed. I was certain that the tickets were hard to come by and pleased that he had gone to the trouble. He scheduled to pick me up at 5:30 for an early dinner the following day.

Matthew showed up exactly on time, looking more casual than I would have expected. I was dressed for the opera instead of a show, and yet again, we were out of sync with one another. Wearing my new, off the shoulder, black lace cocktail dress with an open back might have been a bit much, but it did provoke the desired response. At dinner, he handed me a small box that held a pearl choker. It was gorgeous and seemed to be the perfect accessory for what I was wearing. He stood up to help me put it on. After clasping it, he kissed my cheek and told me how much he enjoyed my company. Matthew said the luster of the pearls reflected the glow of my complexion and that I looked ravishing.

Dying to see how it looked, I excused myself to go to the ladies room. I was overjoyed. It seemed my life had been transformed from ordinary to extraordinary in a single evening without the flick of a magician's wand. For me, the spark of infatuation had been the catalyst. After my first dinner with Matthew, I was revitalized and suddenly, life didn't seem as tough. I'm not certain exactly what it was that caused the change. It felt almost like a chemical reaction. Once in play, everything changed because of it. Although Matthew wasn't all that different from the other men I'd met recently, something with him clicked. Lisa had seen my vulnerability when I spoke about him and tried to rein me in, but it was a futile effort. There was no way I would allow my emotions to be fettered. I knew the rest of the night was going to be wonderful. It had to be. After all, I was with him.

Our dinner was lovely with every detail planned perfectly. The theater was only five blocks away and we had plenty of time to walk there. We strolled at a leisurely pace, until Matthew sped up significantly for no apparent reason. His demeanor changed and when I asked if everything was ok, he responded that it was, but then suggested immediately that we not walk side by side with the streets so crowded. There were not more people on them, than before his mood had changed erratically, and his reasoning made no sense. His demeanor took me back to the night we met. I remembered seeing him talking to himself and wondering if he was just a bit off.

Once inside the theater, he regained his composure and everything seemed to be fine. When I asked why he had acted so strangely, he pretended not to understand what I was talking about. His denial put a bit of a damper on the night, but the show provided the real deluge. It was about a dysfunctional family and revolved around drug abuse and alcoholism. It was so depressing that if a woman hadn't been the lead, I would have sworn Arthur Miller had written it. When we left the theater, both our moods were somber, and he seemed preoccupied when he put me in a cab. Matthew pseudo-apologized by saying he was very tired and needed to go straight home to get some rest. No goodnight, no romance, and no planned next date.

I texted a thank you note about an hour after I got home and received no response. The following night, I called to thank him for the beautiful pearls. It went straight to voice mail. I couldn't understand the distance he kept and tried to find a reason for his behavior, but none was evident. I felt frustrated and confused. Something had changed, but I had no idea what it was.

When we spoke the next day, Lisa asked how the date had been. I told her about the wonderful dinner and the lovely gift. Other than telling her we had not liked the show, I didn't divulge anything about how the date had come to an abrupt end. She was already skeptical about him. Sharing my concerns would have only made it worse.

I left the weekend open for him, but Matthew did not reach out. When I hadn't heard from him in over a week, I called and left yet another message asking that he call me. Trying to show concern, I told him that his silence worried me. I needed to hear his voice to know he was okay. No call came. The week passed without any news and I began to wonder if something had really happened.

My mom used to say it was a rare treat to get every aspect of your life on the right track at the same time. Something was always off. When work was good, you didn't have romance. When your love life was on track, work sucked. When the other two were humming, your health would fail. I had always thought it a bit pessimistic, however, she said if you planned for the worst, you'd always be prepared and might even be pleasantly surprised every so often. She was cautious and didn't give her love freely. You had to earn her trust, but once you did, you were part of the inner circle for life. I would have liked to inherit, or absorb through osmosis, her careful consideration when evaluating situations and people. Always practical and an excellent judge of character, after my mother passed away, Lisa became her surrogate. Before meeting Alan, I had a couple of brief relationships with losers. Mom and Lisa had both seen right through the guys. I had taken Matthew's words to heart without giving myself a chance to determine whether or not he was a good guy, by falling in love with the idea of him. My track record judging men had not been stellar and I should have been careful. As though they predicted it, when my romance evaporated without explanation or any solution in sight, work improved.

Michael and I were civil to each other throughout the week. We collaborated successfully on a project for the first time. Afterwards, he asked me for a listing of my ongoing projects to review. He also requested the marketing calendar and some other data that the department used frequently. It finally felt like he was starting to rely on me more consistently. Since Michael had joined the company, my dealings with Howard became less frequent. Previously, he would always get my take on a problem before making a final decision. After hiring the putz, Howard got into the habit of getting his henchman to gather the data, harvest my ideas, and do his dirty work. I didn't care. As long as Michael and I did not butt heads, our business relationship was tenable.

Lisa had mentioned that she was going to a new accounting software training class close to my office and wanted to meet for lunch. She thought her brain would be fried by noon and would need the friendly distraction. We hadn't spoken much since my theater date and were eager to catch up. Over lunch, Lisa asked how things were going with Matthew. After pausing to temper my response, I told her he was travelling for business and I hadn't heard from him.

She looked puzzled. "That's weird. He buys you this expensive present and then drops off the face of the earth."

"He didn't drop off the face of the earth," I replied defensively. "He's flying all over and I'm certain he is very busy."

"Yeah, finding work-arounds so employers can cheat their employees out of benefits. Prince of a guy this Matthew!"

"Just what it is you have against him anyway?"

"I don't have anything against him, but he sounds so phony. I don't want to see you get hurt again."

"Stop being so dramatic," I replied. "Everything's cool. We should all go out so you can get to know him."

"If you want, but don't expect me to swoon or lie to you about what I think."

"Have you ever?"

"Never have and never will. You act like this guy is perfect. Promise me you'll still date other men and keep an open mind. You can't place all your trust in someone you hardly know. I get a strange vibe about him, just from what you tell me, and I can't figure out why."

"Okay Lisa. I will. As a matter of fact, I already have a date tonight."

After lunch, my afternoon was spent fumfering. I made a conscious effort to work slowly and welcomed all interruptions. The tortoise pace would allow me to cancel my date with the legitimate excuse of having to stay after hours. When Lisa and I spoke, I could explain that I hadn't met Peter because some last minute projects had to be completed and the entire team stayed late to finish them. Before going to sleep that night, I thanked God for the caller identification that would enable me to dodge Peter's calls from that day on.

Right before Michael's afternoon meeting, my phone rang. It was Matthew. Since it was my work phone, I decided to make believe that I couldn't place his voice, though thrilled to hear from him, and asked, "Matthew who?"

"Julie, don't be like that. I can explain - promise. Please meet me for lunch tomorrow."

"I can't, sorry. I've gotta run. I'm late for a meeting."

"Hold on, before you go, give me your cell phone number again. I lost my phone. Thankfully, I just remembered the name of the company you work for and was able to find you."

"Come on, you can do better than that. There aren't that many companies that make handkerchiefs in New York City."

"Please," he sighed. I hesitated only momentarily and then gave in. After sharing my number, I deluded myself into thinking I had done it in order to be on time for Michael's meeting.

The meeting had been brief without many significant issues to discuss. For the last week or so, it seemed Michael and I had called a Christmas truce although we were in the midst of summer. I didn't think it could be possible, but perhaps Animal Planet had been wrong, and a leopard can change his spots.

That evening, I was going out with some of my ex-coworkers for Happy Hour at a bar near my house. Exhausted from the week, I decided to leave early to change before meeting them. When I got to my apartment, I found a bouquet of two dozen creamy white roses on the doorstep with a small card that said: *One for each day I haven't seen you. I'll make it up to you. Promise – M*

He was polished, but the feelings seemed practiced rather than authentic. Matthew acted as though all would be forgiven and I could be pulled on a string. Unfortunately, when it came to him, he was right. The roses were a nice touch and maybe it was true that he had lost his phone. Pushing my skepticism aside, I called to thank him for the flowers and it went to straight to voicemail. Later that day I got a text from him that said:

Can't talk now. Free on Thursday? Dinner?

Sorry, can't.

"How about Tuesday?"

"That might be doable. Let's talk when we get closer."

I was glad to be alone, because like the village idiot, my smile spanned from ear to ear. I waited until some time had passed before calling Lisa to tell her about the flowers. She listened without saying anything, then asked if I was considering seeing him again after his unexplained hiatus. Almost afraid to answer her leading question, knowing my response was not what she was hoping for, I hesitated. My instincts were right, as evidenced by the deafening silence which followed. We continued our conversation, though it was strained, without my admitting to having already scheduled a tentative date with him.

After the call, I wasn't really in the mood to go for a drink, but wanted to catch up with my friends to hear how their new jobs were working out. It was too late to cancel and being with other people might prove to be a good distraction. I showered, then changed into jeans and a short-sleeved tee before heading out to meet the gang.

Along Riverside Avenue, the streets were filled with the happy chaos that is Manhattan on a summer night. Families were packing up their cars for weekend getaways. Singles were starting their action filled nights and city streets were being closed off for block parties.

I had forgotten how much I despised the urban ritual better known as Happy Hour. The bar was packed and there was nothing happy about it. It had been years since I'd been to one on a Friday night and had blocked out the forced joviality of it. Trying to fit in, I looked through the crowd to locate my friends. Within a couple of minutes, I spotted them sitting at a large high-top close to the pool table and waved from a distance while walking towards them. After hugs and boisterous greetings were exchanged, I made my way to the bar for a beer. A tall guy almost knocked the mug out of my hand with a broad gesture as I walked back and my crew could not contain their laughter. We caught up and chatted for a half hour or so, until it became painfully clear that once my coworkers had left the office, we had nothing to talk about. The only thing we had in common was no longer there. Our comradery had been based solely on work. Other than business, we were strangers. They were all younger than me so it didn't take too long to feel like the proverbial third sleeve again. Uncomfortable with the age gap and feeling out of place, I planned my getaway by saying that I had joined them only for a quick beer. I dreamt up a previous engagement to limit the stay of execution. This was more of like a punishment than it was socializing, but everyone pretended to be having fun. It was so crowded that it felt like the subway, with booty to backside people, all jabbering on about nonsense. I committed to having another drink with them and planned on gulping it down to get the ordeal over with quickly.

I thought about walking out but made my way to the bar instead. The bartender was friendly, but the crowd was so loud that I had to yell out my order to be heard. When I did, one of the guys sitting at the bar turned around and greeted me by saying, "Well if the perfume wasn't enough to place you, then the screaming would have been." It was Nate. He and Maureen were on a date and had planned to start it with a drink before dinner and a movie. Maureen's sister from out of town had volunteered to babysit. Relieved when they asked me to join them for a cocktail, I went back to the office group to let them know that my other friends had arrived. I told them that it had been great to catch up and excused myself before heading towards the bar, happy to have made a getaway. There was an empty seat a couple of barstools down from Nate. Being his friendly, forceful self, Nate ended up moving two guys to his right so that I could join him and his wife. Nate was my savior, and as it had been on other occasions, conversation with him was easy. I found Maureen to be equally engaging.

"So, how is life in the single world?" Nate asked.

"It's good. It's really good. Remember the night you gave me a ride to meet a guy from high school for dinner?" I asked and he nodded confirming it. "Well, I've been seeing him since then. He's terrific and I'm really excited about the prospect of having him in my life."

"Sounds interesting. Tell us more," Maureen piped in. "Let's hear about how the other half lives," she said to Nate before giving me her full attention.

I told them a little about the dates, at first not wanting to bore them with details. It had never been my intention to, but I ended up telling them everything, including how strong my feelings were, without obscuring information as I had from Lisa. They also heard about the missed dates, the behavior changes, and the constant apologies which accompanied them. For the first time, I admitted to wanting a relationship but feeling uncertain whether this was anything close to it. Nate made a face like he'd smelled something nasty. When I asked why he was looking at me as he was, Nate replied, "Sounds fishy Julie. I shouldn't be one to betray my own kind, but some guys can be real creeps."

"Here, here," said Maureen.

"No need to gang up on me guys. He's great and you are overthinking things. I appreciate your concern, but really, there's no need." I tried to convince myself along with them that it was all good.

"I don't know Julie. I'd be careful not to let some idiot read your loneliness and treat you less well than you deserve," Nate replied.

"He treats me great."

"Doesn't sound like he does. The flowers are nice, but they might be a Band-Aid to cover up for his many inconsistencies."

"Test him. Next time he asks you out midweek, tell him you are busy and invite him for a weekend date instead. His response will be very telling," Maureen suggested. "If he is missing in action every weekend, it may mean that you are an appetizer for the meal he is getting elsewhere."

"I will. That's a great idea but I'm certain he will pass with high marks. So enough about me, let's hear about you. Tell me how you guys met."

"Laundromat. I fell for her undies before I even saw her. She had these cute little colorful bikinis spinning round and round. It wasn't until later that I found out they were actually her fiancée's."

"Seriously?"

"Of course not. I was doing odd jobs to cover the bills while in school, and she called for someone to assemble an IKEA desk. One thing led to another and before either of us realized it, we were sitting on her couch, completely frustrated, with a half-built desk in front of us and a half-finished bottle of cheap red wine on the floor. With lots of smiles exchanged, I knew she was the one."

"You believe in the one?"

"Of course. If you don't believe that someone was specifically made to order for you, you don't believe in God. He wouldn't leave us to go through it all alone."

I tried to control my emotions but tears filled my eyes despite my best efforts.

Maureen and Nate looked at each other, and then uncomfortably, at me. Trying to focus on the positive, Maureen said, "If it turns out he's not the right guy for you, you'll find the one who is." Clearly, the warning signs were visible to everyone but me. Frankly, I saw them too, but chose to stifle them hoping that wanting a relationship was enough to make it so. In truth, the more I spoke about it, the clearer it became that Matthew's actions were sketchy. His behavior and his words didn't match. It was almost as though he was a puppet, trained to say what the audience wanted to hear. At that moment, everything about him seemed disingenuous.

Sensing tension building, the bartender came over and said, "Nate, this round is on the house. Maybe free booze will cheer her up. Tears are bad for business. Besides, I can't stand seeing a lady cry because her beloved Yankees lost again," he said pointing to the television. It was kind of him to give me an easy out. I smiled as a gesture of appreciation and noticed he was wearing a vintage Tino Martinez Yankees jersey.

"Speaking of the Yankees," Nate started to tell us a story. "There's a little-known fact Maureen doesn't like to brag about. When she was between her junior and senior year in high school, she worked for a limousine service at the Sheraton hotel in New York City. That summer, some of the out-of-town

Yankees' players lived there when they had home games."

Then Maureen chimed in, "Nate can't be trusted to tell it right. I'll take it from here honey. It was a fantastic job, meeting lots of interesting people who came to my desk. One day, a tall, athletic, black man asked me to book a limo to Yankee Stadium for him. I made the reservation. Then, without any further conversation, he asked me to dinner. Hesitating, I paused for too long before turning down the invitation, thanking him anyway. He claimed to have understood but probably misread my bumbled explanation. I would have loved to accept it, but my parents were really strict. I wasn't allowed to date. My dad said most guys were bums. If anyone ever hurt me, he'd kill them and he wasn't ready to go to jail just yet. The bellboy stared at me during the whole exchange. After the customer left, he came up to me incredulously, almost reverently, asking if I knew who that was. I replied 'no' and remained unfazed when he told me it was Reggie Jackson. When I shrugged, he realized that the name meant nothing to me. He said Jackson was the biggest name in Yankees history since Mickey Mantle. I replied that it was good to know and told him that he'd asked me to dinner. His eyes opened up as big as two Oreo cookies. He had already planned to buy a Yankees cap during his break for him to autograph. Shocked when he heard I wasn't going, he just about fainted. I'm telling you, the guy nearly dropped dead," Maureen said laughing at the memory.

The bartender had been listening and was as impressed as Nate appeared to be. He asked, "So you could have been Mrs. October?"

"Yep, but I didn't miss anything. I'd rather have a beer with my hubby than champagne with anyone else," she said candidly. Nate looked a little embarrassed by his wife's loving words in front of others and decided to make a joke of them rather than be called out for his sensitivity. "Sure, that's what she says now, but she dresses up every old timer's day in the hopes of seeing her old flame." Neither Maureen nor I thought it was as big a deal as the men did. Yes, it was a delightful story, but not the life changing event that both guys seemed to think it was.

Maureen had a vibrant personality and didn't seem to take herself too seriously. Strikingly beautiful, it was almost as though she didn't realize it, though she wore clothes that accentuated her dramatic features, like the Kelly-green sweater she wore that evening. It really made her amber colored eyes pop and was the ideal color to show off her brick red hair.

Nate and Maureen spoke quietly for a minute, then asked Joe, the bartender, to pour us another round. Nate said that they were enjoying their beers and had changed their minds about dinner. They would prefer to hang out with me awhile, then go straight to the movie and catch a bite afterwards.

Nate started, "Speaking of the Yankees…"

"We weren't speaking about the Yankees hon. Why is it that men, when given an opening, turn any subject into sports? It's not always about sports," she chided her husband.

"Sure it is. Isn't it Joe? What do you think my better half wants to talk about?"

"Romance?" Joe asked half-heartedly shrugging his shoulders.

"Romance it is," Nate answered. "My grandmother had the biggest crush on Lou Gehrig when she was growing up and mom told my dad she wanted to visit Lou's plaque in Monument Park to see if he was really that handsome. They had their first date there at the start of the season, and when mom recited Yankees trivia as though she had been born in the bullpen, he was smitten. It became a family ritual after that."

He and Joe toasted. "You want romance?" Nate continued, "Ever since pop died, mom and I still go to Yankee Stadium, now accompanied by Maureen and the girls. Each year, on opening day, she still posts a message to him on the fan cam even though he passed away almost 20 years ago. The message is the same each time and reads, 'Happy Anniversary darling, still with us in spirit'. You want romance, that's romance."

It was a sweet story and when I turned to look at Maureen, I saw the appreciation in her eyes.

"They had a wonderful marriage. To this day, the Yankees always remind me of my father in law. He was a terrific man and his son is too."

Again, uncomfortable with the praise, Nate added "I'd like to meet him sometime. Maybe the guy could give me some lessons." She smirked at the joke she had probably heard often.

As we parted, we all said how much fun it had been. Maureen told me they were having a few friends over the following Saturday night. She wanted to meet Matthew and suggested that we pop over for a beer. It would be a fun time for sure and I told her I'd check to see if we were available.

Once home, I called Matthew to invite him to Nate and Maureen's house on Saturday and half expected it to go straight to voicemail. I was pleasantly surprised when he picked up. He had planned to spend that day with me at Dia Beacon, the museum of large art installations on the Hudson. I found it strange that he was setting the agenda without asking if I would be available. I was glad he did. Maybe, he thought that since we were a couple, there was no need to ask. Matthew suggested we do the museum, a quick lunch, and then stop by Nate's house on the way home. He asked how that sounded to me. Anything would have been fine as long as he was part of it. Luckily, I knew enough not to say that yet. I replied that it was a fine idea and asked what time I should be ready and agreed he would pick me up at 10:00 a.m. on Saturday.

I booked a training session with Troy challenging him to sculpt me in a single session. Half kidding, but still wishing he could work magic, I waited for his response. He laughed at my request, but accepted the gig anyway. Some friend he turned out to be!

On the day we were going to Dia Beacon, the sky was overcast and somewhat gray. It didn't matter. I was spending it with Matthew and had been looking forward to our outing all week. I had purchased a new outfit along with a pretty, pastel yellow, summer sweater to wear. Matthew called me when he was on his way. Just hearing his voice excited me. I knew Lisa was right to remind me to slow down, but couldn't help myself. Since I had met the right man, it wouldn't matter at what speed we

126

moved. We were meant to be together. Otherwise, why would we have met up again after so many years? Like a schoolgirl, I created a playlist of mood music (today's version of a mixed tape) to enjoy during the ride up. Lots of songs from our high school days would help us feel young again and bridge any silences during our road trip.

I just finished getting ready when Matthew called. He was waiting downstairs and there were no parking spaces. I bolted for the door without remembering to turn off the lights so he wouldn't be kept waiting. Seeing him, I broke out in an ear-to-ear grin and he seemed pleased with my reaction.

"Hello," he said as he kissed my cheek making my pulse race. His voice had that effect on me. I don't know why, but hearing it for the first time after some days had passed always hit a nerve. We chatted casually as he drove upstate on the Henry Hudson. Making small talk, Matthew commented that it was a shame the weather was so gloomy. I stopped him, by saying it was perfect and told him about my special playlist for our road trip. He seemed amused. It was an odd reaction, but in retrospect, it was understandable. The ride up was shorter than expected. I found that time passed too quickly when we were together and wanted to stop it, to hold each moment a little bit longer. Just as we were crossing the Bear Mountain Bridge, his phone rang and the name Katherine popped up on his dashboard. He became somewhat flustered and allowed it to go to voicemail. Afterwards, he felt compelled to give me an explanation. Matthew explained that Katie was a woman he'd dated for a couple of months about two years ago. He couldn't understand why the dates had meant more to her than they should have. Since that time, she would call every so often. He laughed and said her calls would come infrequently and always at the most inopportune times. She didn't mean anything to him and he knew that in time, she'd grow tired of chasing after him and leave us be.

"Us" I thought. It surprised me that he also felt we were an "us" and it gave me hope. Taking the high road, I suggested that he be kind to her and answer the call without giving her any hope for the future. I wanted to hear the interaction between them to rule out any feelings on his part. Without admitting to it, I said it would speed the healing process for her, portraying myself as a confidant, magnanimous woman instead of the insecure, skeptical one I was.

The rest of the ride was uneventful. When we arrived, he walked around to my side of the car and opened my door.

"Here sweetie, let me help you," he said helping me out of his car. His manners were impeccable and it felt great to be treated with such consideration. He was still an enigma, sometimes thoughtful, then unexpectedly, callous and distant. He was dressed casually and looked more comfortable in his jeans and a Henley. Still, when he walked, his movements were stiff and his mannerisms seemed practiced rather than natural.

Once inside the museum, I sensed that perhaps it was too avant-garde for our taste. The art, if you want to call it that, consisted of large geometric sculptures scattered without rhyme or reason in a cavernously empty, refurbished warehouse. We looked at each other and chuckled. One art snob, who if I had to guess lived in Manhattan on 65th and Park, turned and shushed us. We both laughed out loud and left the room, only to find a similar installation, with more cloned patrons admiring it, in the next one. Matthew reached for my hand and pulled me into a stairwell. Seizing the moment, he kissed me with desperate passion like in the movies, but like in Hollywood, it felt staged. I brushed my doubts aside, letting myself succumb to it. I surrendered my heart and reason along with it. Responding to my question whether he was enjoying the day, he said the museum was not the right place for us. I agreed, thinking we would go someplace to be alone, but Matthew suggested we sneak away to walk through the town and then grab a bite to eat.

I went along with everything he suggested. As had happened in marriage, once I was part of a relationship, I lost my voice and did whatever my partner fancied. We walked through the quaint three block village and stopped at an antique store. He led me inside, guiding me by placing his hand on the small of my back. Looking at the Victorian jewelry, he suggested I select a piece as a memento of our special day together. It wasn't necessary and though the pieces were all lovely, they were also probably pricey. He kissed my cheek again, then walked around the store alone, as did I. When we met up front, Matthew was on the phone and mouthed "business" to me as the store owner handed him a small bag.

He finished his call and told me an issue had come up at the office that needed to be resolved. They were working on a big contract which needed his approval to be finalized, so we would have to leave now. He felt badly that our date was cut short and though I told him it was fine, I was disappointed. He suggested we stop at a deli to get a couple of sandwiches for the road and when he paid the counterman in cash, he said doing so helped him keep track of his expenditures. I thought it was sweet that he felt the need to explain his habits to me. I don't know if my sandwich was delicious or not. To me, it tasted like manna from heaven. The sandwich could have been made of only bread and onions and I would have rated it as three-star Michelin cuisine.

During the ride home, Matthew asked me if I'd see him again. I wondered why he even felt the need to ask, and found myself looking out the window, ruminating about what had prompted the question. The morning couldn't have been better for me, but he looked tense and when I asked what was bothering him, he looked at me oddly and shrugged. While he was driving, I heard the phone incessantly vibrating in his pocket. Pre-emptively, he said, "The pests at work were certain to haunt me, so I turned the ringer off."

As we approached my building, he pulled over and parked. I invited him upstairs, and without replying, Matthew walked around to open my door. He took my hand as we walked up to my apartment. At the threshold, he kissed me chastely on the lips and thanked me for a lovely day. I remember thinking, hey, wait a minute, the date can't be over yet. Trying to squeeze out more time with him, I suggested we meet at Nate and Maureen's later. He hesitated for a moment, then committed to wrapping work up before seven and meeting me there. I jotted down their address and invited him to stay for a glass of wine before going to the office.

"I would love to, but can't trust myself to be a gentleman alone with you. It would be better if I left." I closed the door and wondered who said anything about being a gentleman.

Maureen and Nate were expecting us around six. I didn't want to show up alone and empty handed, so I wrapped a bottle of wine and made a spinach-artichoke dip before heading out. I was glad to be seeing them tonight and looking forward to spending more time with Matthew. I hoped he would impress them and put an end to my doubts.

The party was in full swing by the time I arrived. They had five couples over and were surprised to see me alone. Maureen asked about Matthew, and when I told her about the work situation, she didn't appear to give it a second thought. She was glad he would be joining us later.

Everyone was having fun. They were playing 80's classic rock with the Yankees/Red Sox game on the tube. The mood among their friends was convivial and I was welcomed into their festive circle. By eight o'clock, when Matthew hadn't arrived, I phoned him. The call went straight to voicemail. I texted him then and waited for a response, but none came. Trying to busy myself with something other than worrying about when my date would arrive, I went into the kitchen to see if I could help Maureen with anything. She said no, then changed her mind and asked me to keep her company. She vigorously scrubbed a cucumber as though cleansing it of original sin. When I asked why she was handling it so aggressively, she paused to think about it. After a moment, looking at me seriously, she said, "I am making it organic." We both cracked up. I understood why Nate loved her. Maureen was special. Drying her hands on the apron she wasn't wearing, she asked when Matt was expected. Uncomfortable not knowing the answer to her question, I changed the subject, though not skillfully. Trying to divert her attention, I asked what else needed to be brought out to the hungry crew, and Maureen pointed to my dip as she reached into to the oven, to take out the pigs in blankets.

The Sox were up by three runs in the bottom of the sixth and the men had quieted down, concentrating on the game as though it would help snatch a victory from the jaws of defeat. The atmosphere had devolved from festive to apprehensive, echoing my state of anxiety. While everyone else worried whether the Yankees would pull through or not, I struggled with something not altogether different. I wondered whether Matthew would ever show up. By the bottom of the ninth, I was ready to admit defeat and go home, but Maureen asked that I stay until the game was over, saying it was bad luck to leave when the Bombers were losing. With two outs in the bottom of the ninth, Jeter hit a missile over the white fence façade and scored three runs to tie the game. Everyone jumped up and the crowd went wild. The room erupted in cheers as grown men hugged, laughed, and slapped each other's backs. All were thrilled with the comeback and hunkered down for a long game. When Maureen realized that the extra innings might outlast the food, she decided to order another couple of pizzas just in case. Their friends were in the moment, hoping for a win, and I was still waiting for my hero to show up. Jeter did not disappoint, but Matthew did. For someone who seemed to be concerned with appearances and manners, his discourteous behavior seemed inconsistent with who he presented himself to be. The doorbell rang. Instantly, he was absolved, and I rushed to be there to greet him. Maureen beat me to it. It was the pizza delivery guy. I gave up hope but stayed a little longer to keep up appearances, trying to drown out the voice within before finally conceding defeat and going home. I said goodbye to Nate, who didn't even remember that Matthew hadn't shown. Maureen did. She looked at me with disappointment when she said goodnight, but was kind enough not to say anything more.

Walking home, the streets were quiet and especially serene for a Saturday night. It was that in between time, when it was too late for families to be out and about, but too early for any self-proclaimed partiers to be calling it quits. Things didn't add up. Matthew seemed to say all the right things and appeared really interested when we were together. However, when our time was over, he behaved as though closing a book after reading a chapter. Maybe Lisa was right from the very beginning. I wanted to understand his actions, but was hesitant to delve deeper, afraid of what I would find. It wasn't clear whether we were just dating or in a relationship, and couldn't trust myself to evaluate it in an unbiased manner, feeling the way I did about him. It was likely I would try to excuse his erratic behavior. It was easier to deny it than to examine his actions and find chinks in the armor.

It took me forever to fall asleep that night, turning, and fidgeting while trying to make sense of my romance. I thought it might prove helpful to get someone else's read on the situation. I needed a sounding board, but Lisa found fault with everything he did. She seemed predisposed not to like him, so I couldn't share my concerns with her. Ruth would be a better choice this time around. She would be impartial without knowing my history and might give me more leeway as a result of it. Being older, I thought Ruth would probably be able to give me good advice or share an experience from a similar situation. Organizing my thoughts, cataloging the instances that would best illustrate the reasons for my concerns, I couldn't stop a gnawing feeling from eating away at me. Something wasn't right, but for now, all I wanted was to get a little sleep.

With so many different thoughts flooding my mind, I couldn't relax. Months had passed without any sparks since I started dating. Now that I'd possibly found the right guy, or rather, that he had found me, I didn't want to think about having to drink a lot more coffee to feel this way again. Not ready for another series of bad dates, or the boatload of patience needed to survive them to come this close again, I surrendered into Morpheus' arms hoping to fall asleep. When I finally did, it was short-lived.

I woke up startled and remembered a conversation that had taken place a couple of weeks ago. I surveyed the younger women at work on internet dating and they had eagerly shared their experiences. Over a late lunch with wine on a summer Friday schedule, they claimed there were three types of guys on singles sites.

The more experienced at online dating millennials said there were three types of men on the sites. There was the exclusive guy, who wanted to date only you right from the start. This man professed his loyalty and said he could only see one woman at a time, and luckily, he'd chosen you. Once you finally gave in and dropped your other dates, along with your drawers, the life expectancy of the romance was short-lived. With the perseverance of a Jehovah's Witness, this poster boy would pound your door down until, either you answered it, or it caved in. He would initially say all the right things without twitching or stuttering. He was always exciting and romantic at the start of the relationship.

After the honeymoon period ended, about three months in, give or take a day or two, the real guy surfaced, in his underwear, unemployed, gassy, unmotivated, unkempt, and scratching his ass between burps. "Attila the Un" showed up way too soon forcing you to snap out of the dream. When you asked why he hadn't told you he was unemployed, his reply would be that he had a job. His life's work was to make you happy, and he needed to be on-call, at your disposal full time.

Then there was the romancer. This guy did everything right. He had a bunch of practice. Initially, you would be inclined to think that his actions were natural, but that wasn't the case. He had this dating thing down to a science because he was acting and he knew his part intimately. Like muscle memory from repeating an action, he practiced exactly what to say and when to pause for effect. Playing the part of the perfect man who courted you until you swooned, he planned everything with one goal in mind. Loser number two kept up the act until he had you, at which point he'd lose interest and go back to his married life with two and a half kids, a luxury sedan, and a hefty, new mortgage.

The third bachelor prototype was the serial dater. This guy was polished and smooth. He knew all the newest restaurants and took you to the hippest hidden neighborhood night spots. He wouldn't push you to have sex. He got it so often, that he needed, and wanted, a break. It would end up that you had to entice him, but once you did, he quickly lost interest. Then the thrill was gone and so was he.

Listening to these young women speak, you could only come to one conclusion: most guys looked great initially, but if they looked too good to be true, they usually were. They laughed and said your dream guy would turn out to be a dream, just not the kind you expected. He would be a nightmare. According to them, there were no good men to date online, but maybe I knew better. I'd met Matthew on a site. He seemed to be just the man I was looking for when he actually showed up, or at least, I'd talked myself into believing he was. The gals asked what I wanted in a man. Making certain that my dream was attainable, I said my guy would be attractive, intelligent, had a great sense of humor and great legs to match. He also wanted to be committed. After laughing for a while at my optimism and choice of words, they confessed that finding him would be as easy as finding a Diet Coke in the Sahara. Professing that they knew precisely how it would play out, the gals told me I would find a guy living large through chemical enhancement. His ideal conquest would be between the ages of 21 and 29 even though he was closer to either side of 50. He couldn't fathom himself with anyone in their 40's, so he would feel like he was settling for me from the start. At first, I'd try to make it work by dazzling him. Once I realized that he would drop me as soon as another woman caught his eye, my only interest in him would be to ensure that he got me home in plenty of time to master the new features available on my cable remote - picture in picture, prerecording, and most especially the taping one channel while viewing another option. By the end of the month, I would find these choices infinitely more interesting than chatting up this shell of a man.

By now, my mind was racing. I knew it would be difficult, but I had to get some sleep. I made a cup of chamomile and went back to bed knowing of only one thing that could help knock me out once I was this worked up. So, I turned my television to the Home Shopping Network, sipped my tea, and was out in no time.

Happy to have gotten a couple of hours of sleep, I went to meet Ruth for coffee in the morning and was glad I called her the instant she walked in. Ruth even looked sensible. I counted on her to provide me with valuable input and knew she could deliver. When I told her I'd fallen in love, she responded by asking, "Since I last saw you?" I replied that yes, since then. Her silence prompted me to begin. Rather than tell her who Matthew was, I told her who he wasn't.

"The women at work said there are only three types of men on dating sites. He doesn't fit the mold for any of them," I said satisfied with my preamble but realized without admitting it, that he was a compilation of traits from each.

"Great, so now I know everything he is not. What exactly do you know about him?" she questioned me.

Sharing the details, it became evident how little I did know.

Without giving it further thought, Ruth began. "It is impossible to recognize true love that quickly. Until you've seen a man in a broad array of circumstances, you don't really know him. You've got to see how he responds to stress, sadness, success, and day-to-day life. Notice how he reacts to pleasure and also to challenges. You my dear, are in lust and that's a very distant relative to love. Have sex with him if that's what you want, but don't give him your heart. That is much too valuable to give up so easily."

"And my body isn't?"

"Your body is perfect, but some men might cast that aside in the hunt for something even more valuable to them. If a body were the only thing a man wanted, he would date a younger woman. She would be easier on the eyes, but even more importantly, have fewer opinions and be less demanding. The flip side of that is that this nubile, young lady would also be stronger and have much more stamina. A younger woman would force him to either keep up, or accept that he couldn't, and shut up. An ingénue would be constant reminder of his inadequacies. To some men, that would be devastating. Some men are smart enough to sense it and change their strategy. They go back to someone their own age where they will be able to reign supreme. They fancy themselves lions, stalking prey, waiting to pounce on the most vulnerable. In general, men are more astute than we give them credit for. They are also more like scavengers than lions and can smell out a good match. Like hyenas, men sniff out a recent kill and cackle hysterically when it appears they've scored an easy victory."

"Thanks for comparing me to road kill. Anyway, why do you think I'm easy prey?"

"That's easy to answer. It's because you so desperately want to feel loved."

"And how exactly is it that you come to know this?" I asked.

"Julie, it is very clear that you are yearning for happily ever after and thinking that being in a relationship will get you there. Being in a relationship will only mean that you are in one. It won't resolve the other issues in your life. You need to make yourself happy and find a man who loves you as you are. Only a mature man who is ready to commit, will look at a woman his own age and appreciate the experience and knowledge she has earned from life's challenges. Sometimes, middle-aged men look for lots of flash and don't care that there is little substance. They married for love the first time and even with the best of motives, it didn't work out. Second time around, they go for the game trophy rather than the winning season. For physical appearance, younger women definitely have the advantage. They look pretty, and most, just want to have fun. With them, men only need to show up and pay, which is a lot easier than being present," Ruth said.

"So what are you saying, that only a man who is settling, would be interested in me because I'm past my prime?"

"No, I'm saying that a man who wants adulation looks for a woman who needs to feel loved. He will sweet talk you and if you bite, he knows you are the perfect fit. Is there any other way to see it?"

"You mean that men who are trolling the personals for a 47-year-old just want to feel better about themselves?" I asked angrily.

"No Julia, not all of them, but a man who flatters you constantly and then doesn't follow through, is acting. He is baiting you to see if you'll bite," she continued. "If you do, he feels powerful and secure. Some men need constant reassurance of their virility."

Our conversation hadn't played out as I had expected or hoped. Ruth challenged me and since I didn't like what she was saying, I tried to change the subject, but she kept going back to reinforce the same point.

"You have to get to know a man before you fall in love with him. You know very little about this Matthew and so far, you only know what he wants you to know. Slow down, take your time and keep meeting other men."

"Did you call Lisa and agree on this? That's exactly what my best friend says."

"I guess we both want the best for you then. You are letting your heart lead without knowing if this man is worthy of your love."

"He's a good man," I said defending this almost stranger.

"I hope so Julie. If he is, he'll appreciate getting to know you. If he is not, then taking it slowly will give you time to find out. Relax and have fun. Are you free for coffee next Sunday?"

"Yes, so long as it is not another bloodletting," I said pouting.

"Don't be so thin-skinned. Listen to me. I've lived it. If it turns out I'm wrong, toss out my future recommendations, but promise me, that at least this time, you'll give my advice honest consideration. I'm offering you a free lesson most people learn only after a bad experience, to save you the heartache. See you next weekend my friend," Ruth said as she stood to leave.

After a while, I left as well and walked to the gym for a special class that combined yoga with mindful meditation. Yoga was the perfect remedy for my restlessness since the practice was designed to add a calm balance to a person's life. The class was great. It settled me, preparing me for what followed.

I was eager to calm my thoughts, realizing what a contradiction that was. It was supposed to happen organically, without effort. Meditation began with the instructor asking that we envision something each of us was struggling with, then watch it melt away in our mind's eye. I didn't think the remaining 45 minutes of class would be sufficient to examine my laundry list of maladies.

I listened to the instructor's droning, which began to sound like white noise, in the hopes of achieving a peaceful state of calm. I knew that my mind should be clearing, but rather than thoughts fading into the background, they jumbled together chaotically, bouncing against each other creating more unrest. Everyone else seemed to get it and though meditation was the antithesis of a competitive sport, I was frustrated I couldn't achieve it. Was there such a thing as a meditative vibrator?

Instead, I used the time to try to sort out my feelings. I wasn't being honest with myself about Matthew. I had followed this pattern before. In order to make things work, I overcompensated in the hopes of cementing relationships, both in business and in my personal life. It wasn't the first time that I'd handled more than my share in the spirit of building something together. Unraveling my thoughts about Matthew was like trying to knit with a ball of yarn that a kitten had used as a toy. It was a complicated mess.

The yogi in the background spoke in a rhythmic monotone that lacked inflection and seemed it come from far away. Intangible, it reminded me of dating at my age, but I couldn't wrap my brain around why. I didn't quite fit in – I was neither carefree enough to romp with the younger gals nor old enough to succumb to orthopedic shoes and laxatives. I was the personification of the grim reaper for those searching for passion in a midlife relationship, a misfit with a few wrinkles and stretch marks. The fine lines proudly earned as badges of honor, accomplishment, and experience were viewed by most men as open sores. Older men needed perky breasts and cheerleaders happily yelling "Get it up" to breathe some life into their not so perky penises. Having heard everything from the gentle "too mature for me," which was almost as bad as being called a "handsome woman", to "your pores are too big," or "you're a bit stocky for my taste" deflated me. Talk about picking a partner for qualities that indicated you wanted the same things out of life. Men were dreamers rather than realists, and when it came to dating, for them, it was reality be damned. Despite what they looked like, they still wanted a Barbie doll. A few extra pounds on a partner would come in handy if they were ever out to sea, soon to become shark chum. Still, they couldn't envision the benefits of a more buoyant partner to help them float to shore safely. At least the extra weight could yield a return. What would tiny pores get them? I overlooked ever-receding hairlines for more meaningful qualities like kindness and intelligence. Was it too much to ask for an available man willing to do the same for me?

I heard a bell in the distance and then guided my mind back from hell to the mat. During meditation, I had held a one-sided silent conversation, ranted about men, argued with myself, and thought I'd come to some conclusions. Examining it, I ended up in exactly the same place I had started. Not

exactly meditative, so thanks for nothing Doctor
Peace.

CHAPTER 7

JOB

Matthew called on Thursday to apologize profusely without really elaborating on what had happened. Other than to say work took longer than expected the previous Saturday, he offered no explanation. I thought about asking if he'd been kidnapped for the five days since, but didn't want to take that tone, in case I had misjudged the situation, letting my mind exaggerate the magnitude of the offense. He invited me out for the following weekend, saying nothing could keep him away, and knew he wouldn't have to work too hard to convince me. He was planning the perfect day to surprise me with a fabulous outing. Finally, after all of two minutes, I agreed and we ended the call. I promptly scheduled beauty treatments every night that week. By Saturday, every inch of me had been either buffed and polished, or removed. The "total detailing" was completed when my eyebrows were waxed, lips plumped and hair colored. I even had my teeth whitened. He was going to pick me up at seven o'clock for a light dinner, followed by a movie. More than ready for our casual evening together, his plans weren't exactly my idea of fabulous, but for him, exceptions could always be made. I had been a work in progress all week and was finally ready for the date. At exactly 7:15, he called to say a business emergency had come up. Babbling something about a legal matter on a contract, he said we would have to reschedule. I heard lots of background noise and it sounded like he was calling from the street.

"What contract emergency? Are you recruiting brain surgeons part-time these days? What's going on?" I asked him now irritated, waiting for a response that never came. The call must have dropped, but I wouldn't be silenced and called him back, and of course, it went straight to voicemail.

The jealous nymphs seemed to be working overtime to throw a monkey wrench into things. I tried to believe him, but each time his excuses sounded less plausible. I started to think everyone else had seen through him and judged him correctly.

Since it was the first Saturday of the month, I knew Joey would be playing soccer in the men's league and Lisa was probably free, so I called her. Not wanting to explain, I said, "Hey listen, Matthew had to cancel this afternoon. No, some emergency came up. No, of course not. There isn't anything to be disappointed about. We were just going to a movie. Really, it was nothing special. Can I come over? I can pick up a pie on the way and maybe we can stream a movie."

"Sure thing, but wait a while. The girls are both going to a slumber party and will be leaving soon. I can't wait be rid of them. They've been monsters all week. You can only imagine what it's like when their estrogen is raging out of control at the same time."

"I may not be any better."

"Yeah, but at least with you, a bottle of wine will calm the savage beast. Come in about 45 minutes. I'll uncork the magic potion now to let it breathe."

On the way to Lisa's house, I tried to distract myself from thinking about Matthew. It proved to be impossible. My stubborn streak just couldn't let go of the canceled date. While waiting for the pie, I called and got his voicemail again. Disappointed and confused, I walked to Lisa's pizza in hand. She was eagerly waiting for me holding the bottle of red. I hugged her hard, silently praying that she would not bombard me with a barrage of questions. When she didn't bring it up immediately, I was relieved, until I noticed Lisa had her yearbook open on the coffee table. To me, it felt like being sworn in at a trial, though I'm certain that was not her intention.

"Let's look him up," she said.

"No interest," I lied drawn to the yearbook like a vampire to a blood drive.

"Too bad. I'm looking anyway."

She flipped through her yearbook and when she got to his page, she asked, "This guy? You're kidding! I can't imagine anything good coming out of this," she said circling her finger around his picture. "He was always weird."

He hadn't written anything in her book but we found a couple of pictures of him looking geeky at science honor society and chess club.

"Hey, wasn't he the one who broke Sophie's heart?"

"No, I don't think so."

"Yeah, I'm sure of it. He was the one. Remember he stood her up for the junior prom and then someone saw the weasel with Nan later that night?"

I guess some things never change. "No, I don't remember that," I lied. Though not in the habit of lying to my best friend, I wanted her to give him a fair chance. I had to make sure she didn't think he was a jerk until she had a chance to get to know him and confirm it.

"You're as bad as the girls. You're acting like an awnry teenager determined to get your way."

Lisa had been right about menopausal women and teenagers being kissing cousins. The challenges of finding love midlife seemed insurmountable, creating a mental turmoil that was reminiscent of being a teenager all over again. During both those hormonal harvests, we women, young and old, bend the facts to make them fit our idea of what the world should look like. I was even got acne from the stress of it. Rather than making peace with it, I withdrew and moped around without speaking until we settled in to watch the movie.

I couldn't tell you what the movie was about, but I do remember polishing off the bottle without saying anything else. Having had a little too much to drink, I decided to crash on her couch and get a fresh early start in the morning, but slept fitfully dreaming in 3D about dinner, dating, and being dumped. I awoke in the middle of the night startled, thinking that this guy was either married or in the witness protection program.

I didn't hear back from him that week and fought with myself not to call him. Less than a week later, I lost the battle, but hung up without leaving a message when there was no answer. The very next day he phoned me. The best he could come up with was to say, "I'd lost my phone until this morning and had no way to get in touch with you. I swear you must have cast a spell on me because I'm so forgetful lately. When my pants came back from the dry cleaner with my cell in a sealed bag, I felt like I'd won the lottery. I knew it was a good sign. From now on, these will be my lucky pants."

I listened without saying a word. Enabling him yet again, I wondered if maybe he had early onset Alzheimer's because he was always forgetting and losing things.

"How about I take you away for the weekend? I have plenty to make up to you. I've got a cabin on Lake Winnipesaukee in New Hampshire. What do you say?"

"Let me think about it. I already have plans, but I'll see what I can do, and call you back later."

"Nah, I'm busy later. Call me tomorrow while I'm at work. I'll be counting the minutes."

Lisa had sensed something was not right from the start. Why was it that I refused to see it? I don't know if it was because of my "I can fix him" complex or my bullish stubbornness, but it was not the first time that my will had gotten in the way of sound judgment. It was only after having to shop for Clearasil that I admitted to acting like the 17-year-old he had met 30 years ago.

Though most people hated Mondays, I woke up happy that work would occupy my weekday hours. Weekends were especially challenging when you were single or dating an unreliable man. I went through the day trying not to give the date that never happened a second thought, but around every turn, I was reminded of it when I saw couples enjoying their time together. I knew my happiness shouldn't have been dictated by whether or not I had a man in my life, but for now, it was. I was determined to become as successful by myself in life, as I was in business and was fired up to make it an exceptional day. It was going to be a game changer.

Running into the office ten minutes late because of subway delays, I was immediately called into the CEO's office. Howard could have been Buddy Hackett's long-lost twin brother, except he was fifty pounds heavier, giving rise to the myth that he'd been chained to a refrigerator for his entire life. In spite of that, he was extremely self-confident and didn't let his looks dissuade him from having delusions of grandeur. Though his confidence was misplaced, I envied him and wished some small part of it had rubbed off on me over the years.

Howie was usually a nice guy until either you got in his crosshairs or he let his ego get in the way. You could usually gauge his mood by his posture while sitting down. When he was "going horizontal", it was a sure clue that he was at his egotistical apex. The pose involved occupying the maximum amount of space in his ginormous office by reclining in his expensive Herman Miller chair, with his arms and legs extended so he looked like the bastard child of an "X" mated with the Pillsbury doughboy. He was on the phone. I waited outside his glass door until he beckoned me in. His reclined position prepared me to brace myself for the onslaught. Howard loved having an audience and always put on a good show. It was at those times when he was in his glory. True to his persona, the performance was usually worth the price of admission. I had witnessed him emasculate men, acting as though he was squeezing their balls in a vise. I busied myself by looking around his office, hoping to be distracted from listening to him berate someone, for as long as I could.

I hadn't noticed that Michael was sitting on the couch behind me when Howard had first called me in. When I saw him, it made me realize it was my turn in the vise. Howard apologized for keeping me waiting. It was unusual for him to ask forgiveness for anything. That was my first clue that this was not an ordinary meeting. I knew something was amiss and felt nauseated.

"You know Michael is brilliant and the fact that you two repel each other has been troubling me. For years, I have supported you, sometimes against my better judgment. Michael feels differently and has repeatedly pointed out your shortcomings. Since I'm committed to turning the company over to him, I have begun to filter what I see using his lens. I cannot continue to be loyal to you, simply because of your years of service and seniority with Luster."

With a contrite expression, he lowered his eyes and advised me that my position was being eliminated. Much more quietly, he told me that I was being let go that day. I was stunned and couldn't believe what I was hearing. Half expecting him to say "Happy April Fool's Day" though we were already in July, he had caught me off guard. I couldn't find the words to convey my shock, but in retrospect, realize that my silence probably communicated it well enough. Without responding, I let the silence fill the room until uncomfortable with it, Howard continued. He sat forward in his chair, attempting to look like he was signing legislation and truly engaged. I gulped when I caught Michael's reflection in the mirror, smiling smugly and looking self-satisfied. The fact that he had beat me, pissed me off almost more than losing my job.

"While you've done an outstanding job during most of your time with us, the company is moving in a different direction. Michael is positioning Luster for its next phase and you were not chosen to be part of his team. In part, it's my fault not yours, that you didn't make the cut. I've coddled you for way too long. However, we've structured a very robust severance package for you. Of course, you will be paid for today. In addition to that, we are giving you three additional weeks of pay in recognition of your many years with us. Michael suggested I pro-rate your bonus, as well as your vacation time, and extend three months medical coverage. Julia, he's being quite generous and you should be grateful. I have always liked you and known you to be dedicated, so consider the extra compensation as your bonus for a job well done."

"My bonus, huh? Gee thanks, you're a real sport. Michael most certainly is evolving the company, but not all transformations are good ones. People don't enjoy working here anymore and they are either leaving or have started to punch the clock. He is destroying the company we built and replacing it with a dysfunctional organization that lacks foundation and has no corporate culture. Michael is positioning Luster based on an idyllic company that exists only as a figment of his imagination. His silly dream won't support our very real business."

Without listening he continued, "Julia, I understand you are angry, but regardless of that, if you ever need a reference, please have them call me directly. I'll be happy to let them know about the reorganization and will gloss over your performance issues. I'll tell them that you were a terrific employee and extremely hard working."

"Performance issues? That's bullshit and you know it. There were no performance issues. You're just trying to rationalize a poor decision that was made subjectively."

Michael had picked my brain and gotten the experience I'd acquired over eighteen years in a reader's digest condensed version. I thought we were actually getting along better, until it dawned on me that he had duped me, to ensure everything was in order before booting me out. Michael played me. Even though he considered himself a church-going man, he thought nothing of lying and stabbing people in the back when it came to business. I wondered where in his gospel it said that this type of behavior was okay.

"I'm not firing you. We are downsizing due to unforeseen expenditures and some losses."

"Those expenses were incurred mostly because you and your sidekick decided to build a Taj Mahal of a warehouse. Don't selectively forget that you brought in a difficult to use, unresponsive computer system. To top it all off, you remember this happened simultaneously in the fourth quarter, right? Yes, business was soft but the losses came because your 'investments' didn't allow us to ship some of our customers their holiday orders. Others, we fulfilled two or three times without invoicing. You are making me the scapegoat for your lousy planning."

"Julia, I understand that you are upset but…"

"But nothing Howard. For once, take responsibility for your mistakes so you can look in the mirror and maybe get some sleep at night. Michael may be a genius in theory, but in this industry, he is a moron. And you, you are a self-centered, egotistical prick who leads by intimidation. The only reason you get away with it is because people are afraid to be publicly humiliated by you and those who need their jobs stay quiet. You are incapable of acknowledging anyone else's achievements or recognizing that this company's success was built on the backs of all the people that work here. I'm glad I will never have to see your fat ass again," I said fighting back the tears. I couldn't allow myself to get emotional in front of this most improbable tag team. I was upset, but worked hard not to show it. I refused to give the doughboy and his accomplice the satisfaction.

When I left his office, Howard moved on, apparently without giving further thought to turning my life upside down. He had assumed his favorite position again, probably preparing for his next kill. Had it not been for his big belly, all you would have seen of him at first glance when walking by would have been the soles of his shoes. It was a shame that after I'd left, they were the only souls in the room.

Michael had already asked someone to arrange several packing cartons inside my office so I could move out quickly. He had pre-planned every detail and must have been looking forward to this day for several months. He certainly missed his calling. Michael would have made a perfect secretary, the type who thought of everything without being asked. He had even left me a small hand truck so I could wheel my things out.

As I packed my bags and prepared to go, I heard a loud thud and thought a pallet must have been dropped when the entire floor shook. Almost afraid to look, I turned around to see what had happened, and boy, was I glad I did. The minor earthquake that accompanied the sound was caused by Howard's ass hitting the floor when his chair snapped in two. I guess he'd gone horizontal one time too many. Fat, self-centered bastard that he was, it served him right. I hoped he'd have to sit on a hemorrhoid donut for the rest of his sorry life. Michael was so happy to have gotten rid of me, that he was oblivious to Howard's fall. He sat at the receptionist's desk outside of Howard's Office looking self-satisfied with his arms crossed. It was too good an opportunity to pass up without speaking my mind.

"I wouldn't be so happy if I were you. Yeah Goldilocks, you've eaten your porridge by getting rid of me, but you're still sitting in a receptionist's chair, impotent and at his disposal for the rest of your time here for God's sake. Now that your dream has come true, let's see how it works out for you. I trust your paradise will not be all that you hoped for. Now run along like the sycophant that you are and go help your fearless leader off the floor if you can. If not, call the warehouse and ask them to bring you a forklift to hoist his hefty mass to a standing position. He'll be fine, don't you worry. As for you, now that's a completely different story. I've forgotten more about marketing than you will ever know. You may be book smart, but in my mind, you'll always be an ass."

I walked out with my head held high, closing yet another door on the past. Unlike my marriage however, in this case, I was happy to have had the backbone to speak my mind. I said goodbye to several associates and stopped by Madeline to tell her how much I had appreciated her friendship and support over the last few months. Before leaving, I cautioned her not to let the bastards get the best of her. She was sobbing when she said goodbye, but helped me downstairs with my things so only one trip would be needed.

Once on the street with the personal belongings I had accumulated throughout almost two decades around me, I realized I'd never be able to get home on the subway. I found my phone and rang Nate hoping he was close by and could give me a lift. He had someone in the car, but would be able to pick me up as soon as he dropped off his passenger. It would take him about 20 minutes to get me. I agreed to wait for him and stood on Seventh Avenue feeling lost, engulfed by a career's worth of stuff.

Too stunned from the sting of what had transpired, I hadn't even thought about the financial implications it would have. All I could think about was that bad things happened in threes. So, I counted them off, to make certain the Reign of Terror had come to an end. First, my dating tenure was fraught with more mishaps than had ever been recorded in the tristate area. Second, my boss of many years, had told me I was no longer useful. Third? There was no third yet. I realized I was still in the midst of the perfect storm and stepped back on the curb to prevent becoming roadkill. I braced myself for the third incident, afraid to even think of what it could be.

While waiting for Nate, I called Lisa and she was caught off guard, just as I had been. After ranting for a few moments, she suggested that we meet for a drink as soon as she finished working. I couldn't see myself sitting still until then. My pent-up anger was building to a crescendo. Even when nothing was wrong, I got fidgety without something to do. After what had happened, waiting for anyone was definitely not an option. I apologized to Lisa, saying that at least for now, I'd rather be alone and knew she understood, although she sounded hurt.

I needed a boost and without really understanding why, decided to call Matthew. I was surprised when he actually answered but didn't tell him I'd lost my job. When I wasn't with him, it was easy to see the flaws others pointed out, but when I heard his voice, it always weakened my resolve. It was even worse when we saw each other. This time, he sounded excited to hear from me, and being in the moment, hadn't even realized I was upset. Rather than noticing something was wrong, he went on with his own agenda. Matthew said I had beaten him to the call. He was going to invite me for a drink after work the next day. It felt good to have him initiate the plans, even though I made the call. Maybe seeing him would cheer me up, so I accepted. Sometimes it just took people longer to get to the same place. Since I'd lost my job, that ball wasn't in the air anymore. Perhaps it was my turn to get the golden ring in the merry-go-round of romance.

When asked about my love life, I had gotten into the habit of saying that it was a work in progress. When it came to Matthew, against character, my response changed. I had begun to tell people that I was happy, in a new relationship, and no longer looking. I treated it as though it were a self-fulfilling prophecy. If I said it enough, maybe it would come to fruition.

Nate arrived shortly after my call ended and asked why I was moving so many boxes. I told him. He seemed to be even more embarrassed than I was and didn't know what to say for a few minutes. He drove for a few blocks without speaking, then, without realizing how it would sound to me, he broke the silence with a platitude, saying that when one door closes, another opens.

"Come on – don't give me that. It's a huge, hot pile of horseshit and even you don't believe it," I replied. "Now I have no job, no man and no prospects for either in sight."

"What happened to your high school Romeo?" he asked.

I wasn't sure what to say. If my heart answered, I would have told him how much I wanted it to work. If my head responded, it would speak to all the inconsistencies. I didn't think he would be judgmental, so I recounted the series of events to him and wasn't given the time to ask for an opinion.

"I didn't like the sound of it from the start. Now more than before, this dude seems to be a middle-aged Casanova who is playing games with your emotions." When I asked him if he moonlighted as a private eye, he chuckled in reply. I thought that some humor would make the conversation lighter, but it didn't. He continued pushing me to look at what the possibilities could be. I already knew what the options were and I didn't like any of them.

"You know, my brother has a friend from out of town visiting at the end of next month. I'm supposed to be entertaining him for a few days. We all grew up together. He is super successful and single. Maureen has seen his picture and thinks he is wildly handsome. Why don't you join us for dinner one night?"

"We'll see. With any luck, I'll be working by then and maybe things will have worked themselves out with Matthew. I still think there's a chance for us and see him as someone I could spend the rest of my life with." My words tried to convince myself along with him, but Nate was unwilling to let me off the hook.

"How can you say that? This guy has shortchanged you at every turn and it sounds like he might be playing hide the salami with someone else. What you really mean is, you don't know whether or not your dreamboat is going to ask you out, and if he does, you are going to drop whatever plans you have to be with him, regardless of whether or not he shows."

"That's nasty," I replied, "and unfounded since you haven't even met him."

"I never want to meet the jerk," Nate replied. "Think about having dinner with us when Frank is in town. He's a really good guy."

"Thanks Nate, but I can't focus on that right now."

"Suit yourself, but don't be an idiot. This guy isn't dependable and he's not as into you as he says he is. Otherwise he'd be here," he said pulling over to the curb. "When a guy is interested, you can't get rid of him. I'm just saying, maybe it's time you hang up your stilettos and sit this one out. Some time on the bench will give you the opportunity to recoup and it may even give your eyes a rest so you can open them again and begin to see things more clearly." He had timed the end of his soliloquy perfectly and popped the trunk in front of my building after uttering his last syllable.

Without asking if I needed help, he moved the boxes to the entrance of my building, offering to park and carry them upstairs. I thanked him, then told him I could handle it, not wanting to appear as helpless as I felt. Nate refused to take my money for the ride and said that this one was on him. It was almost 90 degrees out and in the sweltering heat, I made seven trips up four flights of stairs with the boxes. Once all of it was in the apartment, I plopped on the couch and with nowhere else to be, the fact that I'd lost my job started to sink in.

It was Monday, not even noon, and I was already home. Pushing the boxes to the perimeter of my living room, I started to unpack and put everything away, but found that I didn't even want to see my things. These belongings had lived in my office for many years. Seeing them now only reminded me of the job I didn't have and made me sick to my stomach.

I felt stifled inside. It seemed the walls were closing in on me, throbbing to the point that I felt claustrophobic and couldn't get out fast enough. I thought getting some fresh air and looking out on a bigger landscape would help. Changing into a pair of sneakers and shorts, while rushing out of the house dripping with sweat, I closed the door, trying to escape the situation that was consuming me.

I felt drained and had no energy, but as was my custom, I walked briskly and purposefully while trying to organize my thoughts and prioritize the actions I needed to take. I had six months living expenses stowed away in case of an emergency and I could collect unemployment. Financially, I would be fine through the end of the year. However, emotionally I didn't know if I would ever be able to overcome the blow. Now, I was by myself and jobless. What a winning combination! It would make for very interesting coffee conversations. If I thought it was difficult before, what would I talk about now, the cats I didn't have?

CHAPTER 8

JUDAS

As I angrily stomped the pavement and hurried past Starbucks with no intention of going in, someone started tapping on the plate glass window. It was Ruth. Feeling obligated to say hello when she smiled and eagerly waved to me, I stopped walking and reluctantly went to her.

"What a welcome surprise. I'm so glad to see you. How have you been?"

"Just peachy," I replied sarcastically. "I lost my job today, my boyfriend may have someone on the side, and menopause is making me feel like I'm burning up from the inside out. I stand before you like the wicked witch, ready to melt before your eyes. So, thanks for asking, but I'm really not happy with myself or my life right now."

"Where are you going in such a hurry then? Come sit inside where it's cool. Join me and let's chat for a while."

"I guess I could."

"Of course you can. Let's talk through your problems and try to resolve what is going on for you. Together, we'll find a solution. Plus, you'll feel better after you cool off," she said stopping to sip her coffee.

"Ruth, I overwhelmed."

"Stop and take a breath. When we first met, you told me how difficult the environment at work had become. So what if they let you go? Think of it as a gift that opens up the space for something better to fill it. Though it wasn't the right fit there anymore, you didn't make a move. They just gave you the push you needed. Your boss booted inertia in the keister and now you have to analyze whether or not your boyfriend needs the same treatment. Last week, you were on the fence about Matthew's behavior. It's time to start visualizing both the job and the man you want, then work towards making that vision a reality."

I sighed but she continued to speak undeterred. "First of all, Matthew sounds like he doesn't deserve you and he is taking advantage of the fact that you are willing to accept his sloppy seconds. After you reconcile your thoughts on him, the next issue is finding a job, and for that, there is no quick fix. At your level, it will take you some time to find another position. So, sit back and welcome the free time, but don't squander it. Make sure to use it wisely. Do something you've always wanted to, or learn something that has always been of interest. I'll go get you a coffee. How do you take it?"

"Regular to match my ordinary life. Thanks."

She was right. I'd brushed her off last time we spoke because I hadn't wanted to hear what she had to say. I refused to be forced to accept the truth and already knew I had some serious thinking to do. It was time to evaluate my life's trajectory, along with the actions I needed to take, to change it. Sometimes I acted as Howard often did, blaming everyone else for the bad outcomes without really taking ownership for my part in creating them. This was one of those times and though deflecting the pain made me feel better for the moment, it changed nothing in long term.

I had placed all my hopes on Matthew without looking at his behavior and what it meant. The "relationship" was one-sided and out of my desperation to feel loved, I had accepted what little time he gave me willingly. Hesitant to voice my doubts for fear of losing him, I had not demanded anything in return. It had started to feel like most of our dates were taking place only because I accepted being squeezed in on weekdays and didn't make a fuss over last minute cancelations. I had built a few dates into a relationship without any evidence that he felt the same way. Slumping into my armchair, I allowed the heaviness of my thoughts to sink in.

When Ruth returned, she set a designer coffee on the table instead of what I had asked for. She had apparently said something to the barista because he had drawn a frown on the coffee's foam. Isaac had won. He even had me calling the person who prepared it by the moniker he forced down my gullet with the caffeine and it pissed me off just a little. Brushing it off, I turned around to see who was preparing the coffees to thank them. I was surprised to see that Isaac was manning the counter alone. His empathetic response caught me off-guard. Even more foreign to me were his actions. He raised a paper cup in response to my silent acknowledgment of his effort to cheer me up, as though in a commiserating toast.

Ruth and I chatted for some time, mostly about Matthew. After listening to me recount the series of near-misses and recite every lame excuse for his behavior, she said, "Sounds to me like you may be the side dish. It's time to make him own up to his words with actions. You need to get an explanation and hold him accountable. You deserve to know the truth. Everyone does."

After we'd exhausted the Matthew topic, we moved on to my professional woes. Ruth suggested that I take some classes through the public-school system's adult education program. She admonished me for using my age as an excuse for being out of touch. Several years ago, she had taken some courses to become more familiar with computers, and claimed it made a dramatic difference in her life. Ruth was starting to make sense and had given me several good options to explore. She planted a seed that the free time was the perfect opportunity to work on me. I wondered which flaw to tackle first.

When I asked her how she got so smart, Ruth replied that it just came to her on her 60th birthday. I valued having her as a sounding board and apologized for being dismissive last time we'd spoken. She acknowledged that it was difficult to examine situations that were bound by emotions, but said it would do me a world of good if I did. We agreed to meet every Monday morning for coffee until I found a job. She warmly clasped my hand and confirmed my time for java therapy the following week.

I walked home, checked my machine for messages, and then laid out an outfit for my date with Matthew. Even with the entire day to get ready tomorrow, I planned to get dressed in the morning as though still working, not necessarily wanting him to realize my employment status had changed. My title had impressed him and though I couldn't understand why, I didn't want him to know what had happened. Maybe he envisioned me as a successful woman and that allowed him to check off a box on his wish list, or perhaps his business was not as profitable as he let on, and he saw me as a potential crutch. Regardless of the reason, there would be no upside to letting him know that I was no longer employed. The downside was that if my job had impressed him, now that I was not working, he might think less of me. Not saying anything would help maintain the illusion of being successful for a little bit longer.

I spent the rest of the day online looking for a job and registering for unemployment benefits. I cleaned up a resume drafted several years ago when Howard had become unbearable. Then, I set up an appointment to meet with a counselor at the state employment agency before my date with Matthew. It would work out perfectly since I'd already be dressed in business apparel for my date. Getting used to having time on my hands was going to take practice, but I had gotten through day one unscathed and only somewhat unhinged.

The following morning, I walked at a leisurely pace to the unemployment agency, in plenty of time for my meeting, and sat in the crowded room waiting to be called. I was one of the few there who was dressed for business. Sheila, the person assigned to be my counselor, called me in to her office. Dressed in a brightly colored, unconstructed jacket and capris, she looked comfortably fashionable. She greeted me animatedly and shook my hand firmly as we walked towards her office. Looking over my resume, she commented that I was very well-qualified. Then she laid my resume face down on her desk and started to speak.

"Julia, you have enjoyed a long and I'm assuming very profitable career. As I'm quite certain you already know, the retail industry is changing rapidly and it is negatively affecting not only the vendors, but the inter-related businesses as well. I've already had several senior executives in similar positions sitting in your seat this week and it is only Tuesday. It is not going to be easy for you to replace your salary. Marketing executives from almost every industry are out of work with only a handful of positions open. You are going to have to revamp your resume and make changes to the way you present yourself in order to become something other than a commodity. I'm going to give you some pointers and assignments, then set up a standing meeting with you every Tuesday, until we get you gainfully employed."

I nodded and stared at her blankly. It had been quite a while since I sat on the wrong side of the desk. "But with years of experience, shouldn't I be able to find a job quickly?"

"Years of experience make you two things, neither of which is desirable - old and expensive. Here's what I want you to do before our next meeting. Start applying to jobs that fit your skill set. If possible, get an interview or two scheduled. Make a list of potential careers you would like to explore that might fit your future goals, regardless of whether you are qualified for them or not. Keep your spirits up. We'll work through this together."

I stood to leave her office feeling completely demoralized, but thanked her anyway and walked out. With plenty of time left to kill before meeting Matthew, I went to the public library to do some research. It had been years since I'd been there and I felt out of place walking in. It surprised me to see how much the place had changed. When I was working, it was always easier to order books online. Trading cost for convenience would have to become a new habit without a steady income. I walked up to the librarian and asked where the card catalog was. She looked up at me amused, then asked how long it had been since my last visit to the library. As we walked to the bank of personal computers, she suggested we run my card to see if it was still current. Feeling like I needed a passport in a foreign land, my travel guide woke up the screen by moving the mouse to show me how to search for anything I needed. The library was full of surprises. I was in awe of the number of resources that were now at my fingertips. Settling into a chair, I began to search for trending industries. After a couple of hours, I'd learned that other than jobs in medical services, e-com, and the computer programming fields, everything else was trending down. Not thrilled with the prospects, I realized that maybe Sheila was more in tune with the job market than I had previously given her credit for. I printed out the adult education summer schedule and placed it in my handbag. By the time I had finished researching the options, it was still a half hour before my date. I stepped into the bathroom, touched up my makeup, became totally frustrated by my inability to prime the pump at the automatic sink, and left.

Matthew and I had agreed to meet at the Monkey Bar. It was a small locale, but very trendy and already crowded. Most of the patrons were men, and though the few women there were dressed for business, I was the only one who appeared to be wearing a uniform. Other women were dressed in a way that reflected their personal style. Again, I felt out of place. In my suit, I looked like a guy wanting to get in touch with his feminine side. What had previously been the proper attire for business meetings, now felt outdated. Matthew was already there chatting up some chiclet at the bar. When he saw me, he moved back in his seat a bit, and smiled casually.

"Hey baby, this is my new friend Samantha. Samantha, this is my girl."

Closer up, Samantha was an ash blonde with a huge smile and a rack to match. Though mature, she was striking and looked like she would tower over him if he were standing. We nodded to each other smiling as though we didn't mind, knowing full well that we did. Realizing that Matthew was no longer in play, she excused herself and turned her back to start a conversation with someone else.

I looked at Matthew, waiting for him to speak. He said nothing and smiled as though expecting me to start the conversation. He was as handsome as ever, but looked like an out of place schoolboy. It made me uncomfortable. We sat quietly until we ordered our drinks. I was nervous and hoped the alcohol would help take the edge off, so I asked for a dirty martini. Remembering Isaac's theory of what your drink order meant, when Matthew ordered a Gentleman Jack neat, it became apparent that we were polar opposites. "You know Julia, I haven't stopped thinking of you since we met."

"You mean high school?"

"No sweetie, since our first date. I was so nervous around you. I felt like a kid again that night. You know, I had to recite JFK's 'Why Not the Moon' speech three times before we were shown to our table. It's always been my go-to when I need to relax and it was all I could do to calm my nerves."

"Oh, so were you reciting it to Samantha as well?"

He looked puzzled, as though wondering why I wasn't falling for it this time, and floundered, not knowing where to go with the conversation since I wasn't giving him a free pass. Obviously in uncharted territory, he was unsettled and visibly struggling with what his next steps should be. Seeing him squirm felt good, like payback for all the times he had left me hanging. Uncomfortable with the situation, he excused himself and went to the bathroom.

After a few minutes, he returned looking like he had washed his face and run wet hands through his hair. He sat down again. Matthew carried on, pretending he had just arrived, making believe he could rewind the clock. Talk about an alternate reality! He battled on relentlessly, baiting me with compliments until we both started believing them. After that, the conversation seemed to flow more naturally. We chatted casually for another 20 minutes or so before he could see the lure starting to work. As soon as he did, he invited me to New Hampshire for the weekend again, telling me about what he had planned for us even before I accepted. It sounded wonderful only because it appeared he was now thinking committed relationship, like I had been since our first date. Against my better judgement, I let my emotions be swayed. I was giving him a mulligan and we both knew it. After two more cocktails, about an hour later, he stood up, saying he had an early morning the next day, and offered to walk me home. I accepted, thanking him, and we started making our way to the door. He guided me possessively through the crowded bar, by placing his hands on my hips while directing my movements from behind. The intimacy of the gesture felt sensual. It seemed we were finally moving past the awkward stage of not knowing what we meant to each other.

The bar had become even more crowded and the way out was an obstacle course littered with trendy New Yorkers. I was glad it was packed. People involved in group conversations prevented a clear path to the exit. It proved difficult for them to move out of our way, and prolonged our time together, until the sea of humanity parted for someone pushing to get through the crowd. A woman, looking doggedly determined and half crazed, walked right in front of us. Planting herself firmly as a barricade, she became a permanent obstacle forcing us to come to a complete stop. I didn't mind. Matthew's hands were still on my hips and I wanted to keep them there for as long as possible. The woman, wearing a ponytail and a softball jersey, stared at Matthew, her eyes bulging out, as he quietly said, "I can explain Katie." His palms became sweaty and he dropped them to his sides as he stepped towards her, leaving me behind.

"Working late while I was at practice, huh?" She was shaking with anger. While staring at me, but addressing Matthew, she asked, "Aren't those the pearls I thought I lost on our vacation a couple of weeks ago?" He lowered his head but did not reply. She turned to leave visibly upset and walked halfway to the door, then changed her mind. Instead, Katie faced the bar where she conveniently found a half empty pitcher of beer. A menacing smirk crossed her lips as she turned towards him. She composed herself, then would up like she was pitching in the World Series. Clearly at the top of her game, she unleashed a furious fast ball of ale, pitcher and all, dousing him. I don't know whether the pitcher shattered on his lovely nose or when it hit the floor, because by then, the crowd was roaring. The bartender called out, "I told you it was just a matter of time Matt. You should have known it was bound to catch up with you. Next drink is on the house for the collateral damage!"

KKKatie threw a set of keys at him and said, "These won't work by the time you get home and by the way, neither will the ones to my father's employment agency when you get there tomorrow morning."

I didn't ask, and he didn't tell, but it was obvious that the weekend would never come for us and that whatever I thought we had was over. He stood there in disbelief, giving new meaning to the expression beer-battered, while trying to look like he wasn't flustered. As I walked out of the bar, the blonde he had been flirting with, grabbed a bunch of napkins to stem the surge of blood from his nose, while attempting to dry his face with the napkin in her other hand. He must have been in pain but smiled disingenuously allowing her to fuss over him. He had his hands on her waist and I sensed he was marking the territory around his latest conquest. Walking home alone, I wondered how empowering it must have felt for Katie to do what she did and hoped for her, that she would hold her ground without giving him another chance. In my mind, she had closed the game and deserved to walk off proudly.

I got home drained from the events of the day, to find my answering machine blinking with a message.

"Hey, Jules. It's me. I'm sorry I've been so negative. I'm sure Matthew is fine and I'm overreacting. I just don't want to see you get hurt again. Call me when you get in. It doesn't matter what time it is."

I waited a couple of hours and called after I had finished my dinner.

"Lis, please don't apologize. Maybe you were right. Yeah, he asked me away for the weekend but I'm leaning towards not going," I said not wanting to come clean about what had happened. She had been right from the start. I replayed the events, trying to see if there was a way to soft-peddle it, then reconsidered, knowing there wasn't any explanation for it other than what it was. He was cheating on this woman with me. Talking about things more openly with others had felt good. I took a leap of faith and proceeded to open up and come clean with my friend, telling her the details of my short and sordid evening.

"What a weasel! He must do this often. I'll bet you he's married and that was his wife," she sighed. "You see what I mean? The shiny penny is more attractive than all the rest, but after all is said and done, it's still only worth one cent. You just have to learn to leave those on the floor."

"I know. What is it about me that attracts only losers? Do I have a target on my back or do I just scream out lonely?"

She said, "Spin around." Come to think of it, her next words were probably the impetus for face time. As though I was with her, she said, "No bulls eye, but you do have a taste for losers. It's time you change your diet. It was clear from the start that he was a cheat and a player. You deserve way better than that."

It took all my strength and my best friend's tongue lashing to force me to see all the previously disregarded warning signs. I admitted to overlooking them willingly and was glad my new superhero, beer-woman, had surfaced when she did. I had come too far to settle for someone who respected neither himself nor me. At best, he was juggling a couple of women at once, and frankly, I was too old for that shit.

With the later part of the evening to myself, I turned on my laptop and decided I'd search the job sites to set up some interviews. No new positions had been posted. There were only two jobs that potentially interested me, so I applied to both even though I thought I was overqualified for either one. At least getting an interview would allow me to get comfortable with the process again.

The radio droned on in the background. The talking heads said the unemployment level had hit a ten year low at just under five percent. It felt like I was the only person in all of New York who was unemployed, even though earlier, Sheila had alluded to the glut of people looking for work. She had explained that the unemployment percentage quoted in statistics was historically low because the state only counted payments made. It didn't take into account the many people who had not been working for so long, that they had run of out benefits. Subsequently, they had fallen off the map and were not considered out of work. Shelia added to that figure the large number of executives who were under-employed, which I came to learn meant working either part time, or for way less than they were worth.

It was already late and knowing I wouldn't hear back at night, I decided it was time to turn in. I tried to sleep but couldn't get comfortable in bed. Not only was I crushed to learn that Matthew wasn't even a cheap knock off of what a man is supposed to be, I was also finding out that getting a job wouldn't be as easy as I had imagined either.

In the morning, I felt like forty miles of bad road after the emotional marathon from the day before. At least it was a new day. I wanted to treat myself to some pampering to help heal my bruised heart, but unemployed and strapped for cash, I wasn't comfortable indulging in something extravagant and couldn't think of anything inexpensive that would have made me feel better. Well, yes, I could, but without a partner, even that would be tough. I walked to get a coffee and grunted what might have been mistaken for a hello to Isaac.

"Good Morning Rapunzel. Somebody steal your brush?" he asked. It wasn't until he said it that I realized I must have left the house without brushing my hair. It was disconcerting to see how much not having my workday routine disrupted my life. Adding some structure back in would help me regain some semblance of normalcy without an over-scheduled appointment calendar to regulate my days. I felt disoriented and was uncomfortable enough without Isaac's incriminating stare as he handed me my coffee in a bag.

"If you take it to go so you don't scare off my customers, it'll be on me today." Unsure of myself and somewhat embarrassed, I wondered if it was his way of treating me to my morning Joe since I was unemployed, or if he was taking pleasure in ridiculing me because I looked homeless. No matter what it was, it was easier to take him up on his offer than to wither away under his scrutinizing gaze. I walked out defeated, and with nowhere to go, found myself walking across the park and sitting on a bench with an old man who was busy feeding the pigeons part of his bagel.

"Beautiful day, isn't it?" he asked in a friendly manner.

"I hadn't noticed," I replied honestly.

"I'm always amazed when young people don't take the time to enjoy each day they are on this earth."

Great, I thought to myself, I'm probably sharing the park bench with a just released convict or a bible thumper, but I did appreciate being called young for a change.

He extended his hand and said, "I'm visiting my daughter who just had a baby and it's my first trip to New York."

"That's nice," I replied curtly so he wouldn't get the idea that I wanted to engage in conversation. Apparently, he got my message because he didn't say another word to me. We sat in silence, two strangers on a park bench, for what might have been as long as an hour.

Before he left, he stood and said, "I'm sorry you are having such a bad day miss. I hope it gets better for you."

As he turned to leave I thought about how poorly I'd behaved. Not wanting him to think everything people said about New Yorkers was true, I caught up and started walking slowly beside him as my form of an apology. Waiting for an invitation to pick up where he had left off, we walked together for a while without saying a word. It was he who broke the silence by saying, "Don't worry. It's okay. There was a point when I didn't know that my attitude

174

would determine how I would be treated by life either."

"What do you mean?"

"Well, let's see how best to explain what I've learned. Life reflects your demeanor back, like a mirror, and if you give out only anger, it is certain to bounce back tenfold."

"Do you know where you are going?" I asked wanting to make amends.

"No, but I was hoping you could give me some pointers. My daughter isn't meeting me until lunchtime," he said.

"Where do you need to go?"

"Need to go? Nowhere right now. I was just enjoying the day when you joined me on the park bench."

"Would you like to walk with me?" I asked.

"Certainly. You can give me the insider's tour of Central Park."

"I wouldn't know where to start."

"Start right here. I believe we are close to the children's zoo and the Alice in Wonderland cuckoo clock."

"We are. It seems you know more about the park than I ever will, but I'll give it a whirl. What would you like to know?"

"For starters, why are you so angry and frustrated when you have so much going for you?"

"So much going for me? That's a laugh. Your visit to New York isn't long enough for me to begin listing my woes."

"David," he said extending his hand.

"Julie," I replied as we continued to walk towards the zoo. It was not crowded that day and with no attendant to collect tickets at the entrance, we walked right in. I told him how the zoo had recently been updated and park traffic had increased because of it. As his tour guide I continued to talk, finding him easy to speak with and very relatable. Like when going to confession, behind the screen of anonymity, it was less difficult to express my feelings. With David, I gave voice to them quickly, with ease. It felt as though my secrets would be safe. Even if they weren't, who would either David or the polar bear tell that I could give a rat's ass about? After telling him about the time capsule buried in the obelisk, I felt less vulnerable and unearthed my hidden feelings, recounting all the times I felt wronged recently. With most friends and business associates, I generally kept my heart guarded, putting on a mask that showed only what was expected of me. Opening up had been cathartic. Purging the thoughts that had been consuming me, I told him about losing my job and how humbling it had been. Continuing the tirade, I verbalized how I had allowed my career to define me. Then, I went on to explain how dating had fallen short of my expectations. He continued listening intently. When I stopped for a moment, he jumped in quickly, as though thinking that if he didn't, he might lose the opportunity.

"There are some things only time can teach. The shame of it is that by the time we learn, we are sometimes too old to put the knowledge into practice."

"My friend Ruth says that knowledge comes only from experience."

"In part, but it's much more than that. There are moments when I feel God did it backwards. I'm borrowing from Shaw, who was rumored to have said it first, that 'Youth is wasted on the young.' Sometimes I think that we should have been born old and become young so we can make use of all the knowledge we gain along the way. By the time our hearts and minds are open, our bodies are sometimes too old or feeble to execute the vision."

"Boy, do I know what you mean - that explains my feelings perfectly. I'm feeling ancient lately and hadn't taken into account how nice it would have been to know what I know today thirty years ago. I'll have to remember it. Thanks for sharing."

"Nonsense. You still have plenty of life to experience. Listen to me and stop behaving like a bitter old woman. You seem to be closed off to experiences and are probably so busy feeling sorry for yourself that you are missing out on the opportunities available every day. I'll one-up Shaw and say that life is wasted on those who concentrate on the negative. There will always be enough sorrow to go around. You don't necessarily have to look for it, but by not dwelling on the bad, you open the space up for something good to happen. The sad thing is for many, every day is a further departure from being in the moment and enjoying the ride. We all need to stop, pause, press reset, and learn to appreciate engaging with each other again. As a society, we spiral from one activity to the next without enjoying all that we have in life."

"Do you see me that way?"

"Well, for starters, you just met me and unleashed about a month's worth of fury on me. You have so much to be grateful for and don't seem to know it."

He was right. There was no denying it. My frustration had taken charge of my larynx and maybe I had missed out on some things because I was too busy being angry.

"When you question and learn, life can be very rewarding, but it's is important that you share the knowledge with others. Look at the way animals teach behaviors to one another. Over there, the monkeys are grooming each other and the young learn by mimicking their elders' actions. They share insight as our mothers did when we were young. The problem is that once we are out of school, learning stops for many people. If my voice could carry more, I would tell everyone to enjoy their adventures instead of posting them. Instead of Snapchatting a flower, smell it and enjoy its beauty. Eat your meals rather than uploading them to Facebook. Savor the moment and live in it.

"You sound like a new-age hippie."

"Anything wrong with that?"

"No, but it is just not the verbiage I expected to hear from someone your age."

"That's exactly what I mean. Don't prejudge people. Learn from them. Let them speak and listen not only to their words but also to what remains unsaid. These things will be much more indicative of who someone is than how they look. Get to know the person before passing judgment."

"I know you are right. God knows I've heard the same thing said in different ways often enough lately."

"Now, would you indulge an old man for a moment?"

"Of course."

"Nothing happens by chance. Maybe our paths crossed because we were meant to meet today. Be more attentive to the hints life gives you along the way. They will prove to be invaluable and don't close any door before you get a glimpse of what is on the other side. Catch curiosity and spread it."

I listened as he continued.

"You must learn from everything life decides to share with you – good or bad. Don't frighten others off before they can even get close. You almost did that to me today. Decide right now to live the rich, full life you were put on earth to enjoy."

I leaned in and kissed him on the cheek thanking him for holding up a mirror to my behavior and for allowing me to walk with him. I appreciated the time and wisdom he shared. As we stood saying goodbye, a young woman pushing a stroller approached us.

"Hey dad, who is your new friend?" she asked in the form of a greeting. She went on to say that as always, he was late because he was changing the world one person at a time. She nodded hello, extended her hand, and introduced herself as Nora. "Sorry to run off, but we are already late," she said taking her father's arm as they walked out of my life. I never learned who David was, but I envisioned that he had accomplished much in life and vowed to take his message to heart. After all, how many different people needed to beat the same lesson into me?

I had no idea what time it was or even how far we had walked. I forgot how angry I'd been earlier and pondered the insight a stranger took the time to share. Walking outside of the park towards my house, the sky was a myriad of colors. The sun that had broken through the residual morning clouds was starting to set. Relishing the colors of the sky as the evening took hold of the day, I felt poised on the brink of change.

CHAPTER 9

JUDGES

While walking home, I noticed a banner on a storefront that read "Family Friends - Welcome". Heeding David's advice, I walked in to see what it had to offer. From outside, the location looked like a shop, but I came to learn it was an animal shelter for homeless pets. It had opened about a month before. The frenzied attendant was bathing an unhappy dog, but extended her hand to shake mine anyway. Realizing it was full of suds, she withdrew it and introduced herself by saying, "Hi there, I'm Lynne. Welcome to Family Friends!" I smiled in response and waited to see if she was going to show me the place, but Lynne was busy and suggested I look around until she was free instead. She pointed to a counter in the corner where I could help myself to a beverage.

As I poured myself a coffee, Lynne's cell phone rang. She apologetically asked if I could answer it by simply saying Family Friends, then requested that I relay the conversation to her in real time.

"It's Joan. She has to leave town for a last-minute business trip. She's really sorry, but she won't be here for the next two weeks. It can't be helped."

"Please ask her if she has any friends who can fill in for her," Lynne called out to me.

I did so, then advised back that she did not. After hanging up, I heard Lynne talking to the dog she was bathing. "Great, I finally get a volunteer to help and she can't even make it here on the first day. We are just getting started. You know I could really use the help. How are we supposed to get this place off the ground when it's just you and me again, Chasie?"

Lynne seemed frustrated, and it was easy for me to commiserate with her disappointment in people. I thought about helping out just for the day. With nothing else to do, there would be no harm in offering. "Hey, I've got no other plans this afternoon and can give you a hand if you want."

"Really? That's fantastic! Joan was the second volunteer to cancel last minute. My only full-time employee changed her mind about working here after realizing that dogs poop. Roll your sleeves up and we'll get to know each other while we give the pooches a bath."

"Ok. I'm Julie by the way." Hesitating, I continued, "Hey, is there something else I can do though? I've never given a dog a bath and am not sure how to."

"There is nothing to it. It's easy. All you need to do is accept that you'll get doused a few times before you learn to keep them under control."

"I'm willing to give it a try as long as you don't mind a little bit of a mess."

"Deal. Grab the shampoo and let's start you with the easiest dogs. First bathe Amelia, the Mini German Pinscher, and then Max, the Scottie. They will be really easy to deal with and since both are being adopted today, they need to look perfect. I'll get the last one. He's a handful, but is super sweet and a big mush." She realized that I didn't know the differences between breeds when I hesitated, so Lynne pointed them out to me. After bathing the one she was working on, Lynne got the next dog ready.

"My God he's huge," I said a little too loudly. "He looks mean."

"Why, just because he's big? Looks can be deceiving. He's a Rhodesian Ridgeback mix. If he wanted to, he could do considerable damage with those jaws, but it's not his nature. The biggest ones usually think they are lap dogs. Watch this. Rocky, come here."

He walked over obediently and stood close to Lynne, waiting for her direction. She tapped the side of the tub and though you could see the dog didn't want to, he climbed in. Without being happy about it, Rocky obeyed her instructions just the same. He was so happy with Lynne's praise that he seemed to have forgotten about his hatred of baths.

As we bathed the dogs, Lynne told me about herself. She was a pediatric nurse in the neonatal ICU at Mount Sinai and volunteered here during her free time. Lynne worked twelve-hour shifts, but only four days a week, so she had plenty of time to dedicate to the dogs. She told me her job was often stressful. She confided that though she loved nursing, sometimes she felt powerless to help some of the infants. Despite the technological advances in medicine, it was still God who had the final say. At least with the dogs, she was able to find many of them the homes that saved them from certain death. Caring for the dogs provided a good way for her to unwind and the shelter established a happy balance in her life.

"With the kids, I feel my job is to minister to their needs and help them get strong enough to go home. Some are just too frail. The only thing I can do is make them comfortable and support their parents. After twenty years in nursing, it still breaks my heart each time we lose a baby. At least here, I have more control over the outcome. I have always wanted to open a shelter. Even for the ones that are not adopted, now, I can still keep them alive."

"I don't know how you work with helpless infants every day knowing there will be some that won't make it despite your best efforts. It sounds emotionally draining."

"It's tough," she replied, "but it can be very rewarding. It is a big win when we are able to make sick babies well and get them home. What do you do?"

"Well, I used to work in marketing for a wholesale company, but right now I'm out of work."

"That's too bad. Did you love the work?"

"I used to. Recently, a management change disrupted everything and took the joy out of the job. As though that weren't enough, online shopping is nearly making my entire industry obsolete and getting a job is close to impossible."

"What kind of job would make you happy?"

"I don't know. I guess I'm still a work in progress. Maybe being a taste tester for Ben & Jerry's or being a lottery winner if those are jobs."

"Having some time to think about it may be exactly the right thing then. You have to enjoy what you do since you spend more hours working than doing anything else. My calling has always been to work with both kids and dogs."

"Now that you put it that way, maybe writing copy for handkerchief packages wasn't a lofty goal."

"It doesn't really matter what I think of it. What is important, is how you feel about it."

"Well, it always provided a good living but it would be nice to do something of value like what you do," I said soaping up the smallest dog.

Lynne talked about the dogs as though they were people. As I bathed Amelia, she told me her story. She had been a street dog. I saw part of her ear was missing and several scars marred her legs. It was clear by the way that Amelia hung her head that she didn't care for the water either. Lynne said she would make a great addition to someone's family because she had gone without for so long, that now she was appreciative of any attention or care and would surely return someone's affection tenfold. Gratitude was a powerful motivator. It was evident that it had already helped create a strong bond between the dogs and their caregiver.

Each dog had a unique personality and Lynne seemed to relate well to all of them. Even Max, the Scottie, who embodied the personality of a crotchety old man, reminded Lynne of her grandpa. She had grown fond of him in no time and gave him special attention because he was the senior citizen of the pack. He relished the affection though he didn't show it most of the time. He appeared to be very aloof, however, when she stopped touching him, he would put his paw on her forearm to remind her that he was there. People and dogs weren't so different from one another after all.

Lynne and I worked well together and became friendly in short order. It may have been the collaborative effort that cemented the friendship. She was easy to talk to and had a calming influence on me. I was enjoying myself and actually didn't mind bathing the dogs.

"You know, it's strange, but I find it really relaxing to be here," I said.

"Nothing strange about it. There is a treatment called Equine Therapy that soothes people by having them care for horses. The task of grooming them is time consuming and tedious but the repetitive action brings them serenity and speeds up the healing process. The routine helps people come to terms with whatever they are dealing with. Sometimes, caring for someone other than yourself can be very rewarding."

"I've never had kids or a pet. It always seemed that it wasn't the right time."

"That right time, right man, right job stuff is bullshit," she said waving a soapy finger. We both cracked up when she mistakenly flicked some dirty dog water on me.

When we finished bathing all the dogs, it was almost 8:30 p.m. – past dinnertime at Family Friends. We fed them quickly and then walked them. By nine, it was time to close up shop. Lynne told me she usually stayed there until about 10:00 to finish up paperwork and to walk the dogs again. She liked staying with the pups for a while longer and never wanted to leave them alone longer than necessary. They got lonely and besides, she was going home to an empty apartment so the company was good for all of them. I knew the feeling well.

"It concerns me that we haven't gotten many adoptions yet. After putting so much work into this, I want to see it succeed. I think about things I can do to drum up traffic even in my dreams, but it is taking people too damn long to find out about us. This is something I've always wanted to do. God knows I'm giving it my all, but can't figure what I am doing wrong."

"Why is it that women always blame themselves and men usually blame someone else? You are doing nothing wrong. I think this place is great. The news will spread, don't worry. Once people know you are here, you'll have more demand than dogs!"

"I also need to get financial support from people in the neighborhood and local shops. Hey, since you are a marketing guru, let's formulate a plan on how to get the word out tomorrow. See you then," she said rather than asked.

I don't know whether I committed or she forced the commitment on me, but either way, it was fine. I enjoyed helping.

I was glad to have the dogs to occupy my time because the dating scene had slowed down to a trickle. Women who had been through it before said it came in waves. Right now, it was more like a mirage than it was like the ocean. Family Friends became a haven that gave me a much-needed place to go where I felt useful.

Even the job sites had dried up and didn't hold much promise. I laughed when I thought of how fitting the phrase "The Dog Days of Summer" was this year. The only jobs being posted were for junior positions and once recruiters looked at my resume, they didn't even consider me. They must have thought I was too old, too expensive, and too set in my ways. Each day, the news about more stores closing, provided a graphic illustration of how consumer spending had dramatically deteriorated and shopping patterns had changed. My future looked as dismal as retail's.

Without much else on my agenda, I continued to volunteer for the next couple of weeks. I created some flyers and distributed them to the stores with the most traffic in the neighborhood. I felt good about making a contribution and hoped to see positive results from my efforts. Lynne and I got along well. As I got to know her better, my respect for her dedication grew. She knew what was important and had the right priorities. Though Lynne was not married, she had created a family by converting strangers into friends and it made for a better life.

Each time I left Family Friends, I wanted to take as many puppies as I could scoop up in my arms and run. Of course, it wasn't the puppies that really needed adopting. It was the older dogs. Not as cute as they once were, with bad habits reinforced by being isolated in cages, they were difficult to place. The incessant barking all around caused them to be skittish and made bonding with them more difficult. In addition to being old, most were big dogs and in New York City, where people lived in apartments, size mattered.

The long-term residents were usually pit-bull mixes who got a bad rap because of dog fighting rings. They were thought to be aggressive by nature, but the behavior was not inherent in them. Abused and malnourished, anger had been beaten into them. Once removed from that environment, they learned to trust again slowly. When given love and appreciated, I was told they reciprocated with devotion and unfailing loyalty.

It was the bait dogs that I pitied most. These dogs had been trained to be submissive, so the other dogs could build their confidence by mauling them easily. It broke my heart each time I saw one. They were so used to being attacked that they accepted it. Cowering and fearful, they didn't even put up a fight. They were products of their environment. Bait dogs had many scars and looked older than they were. Their eyes were vacant and without hope. Judged by their looks and immediately cast aside for the younger, friskier ones, they were used to being passed up. I understood them. For the ones who got homes, being patient had paid off. Though rejection had always been tough for me, their journey gave me hope. I was able to relate better to the dogs than to most people. I didn't have to explain my feelings to them, they simply smelled them and understood. The dogs were the best part of my life, and at the time, it was enough.

Since my divorce, I saw friends on occasion, but our lives intersected more than they were shared. I had nothing to contribute it seemed, so retreating was a natural response. My acquaintances allowed me to do so not wanting to make me feel uncomfortable. I couldn't blame them. If you were happy and busy, the world seemed to organize itself around your schedule. It was hard to visualize things from someone else's perspective. Having always measured my value by my work, a higher paycheck equated to having more to offer and being unemployed had magnified my insecurities. It also stirred up feelings of worthlessness. The worse thing about not working was that it made me feel vulnerable, a feeling I hated. I learned to accept things that were out of my control and was just starting to find out how many of those things there were.

Not being a webmaster, capable of creating apps, or savvy at social media, my workplace value was limited. The world of the future seemed to have left me behind. Like it or not, I accepted some of the blame, realizing that in part, it was my own doing. I didn't even understand many of the job descriptions and wondered if my usefulness had been outlived. I needed to find a way to regain some self-esteem by marketing myself differently. Though it didn't feel that way, I was an expert in the wholesale marketplace who had lots to offer. I had to believe that even if nobody else realized it, my knowledge and years of experience made me a rare find for the right company. In some ways, looking for a job was like looking for a partner. It was all about finding the right fit. With my background, it should have been easy to excel at both, but it wasn't. The divorce and losing my job made me doubt myself and it was tough to sell yourself when you felt like day old bread. How could I move past that to convey that I was worth employing or loving if I couldn't confidently utter the words "Take a chance on me and you won't be disappointed"? For the dogs, it might have been easier. They did it with their eyes.

The week progressed without any fanfare. When Sheila and I met, I told her that if I didn't find a decent job soon, I'd have to start withdrawing from my savings. It went against every financial planner's advice, especially at my age, but given the situation, I didn't have alternative options. I couldn't live on my unemployment alone and dreaded thinking about what would happen when my rainy-day fund was depleted. Applying for any job that seemed like it had potential, as I'd been doing for weeks, just wasn't working. At one point, I was considered blue chip and recruiters called me.

Now I felt like an undervalued penny stock and seldom even received a call back. I was told summers were the worst because there were more candidates in the field due to the recent graduations. With many hiring managers on vacation, it felt as though I wasn't considered worthy for any job. Companies were looking for graduates right out of college who would be eager to earn their way by working nonstop to get ahead. The computer skills that were as natural to them as breathing was to me, were what was highly valued. Sheila mentioned that instant messaging had even infiltrated the office environment when she forewarned me to it step up. She suggested I register with the labor department for some free technology classes and also that I stop dressing like her grandmother. I countered by saying that business apparel was always appropriate in an office environment, like a little black dress at a cocktail party.

"Julie, open your eyes and see what that means these days. Time to go shopping with a friend who has great taste and style."

For me that was Ruth, but I protested saying, "There will be no shopping until I find a job."

"And there won't be a job unless you go shopping first. You can take that to the bank," Sheila stated. "Catch up with the times or watch life pass you by. What was in fashion and deemed valuable last season is now antiquated and without value."

After the disheartening wake-up call, I checked my email the instant I got home. My inbox was filled with junk. I began applying for any job where they'd accept a middle-aged warm body to fill a seat. I was almost ready to accept a job as a Wal-Mart greeter, when surprisingly, an email came in that held promise. It was from the human resource manager at a major apparel maker. He provided his number and asked that I call him to discuss the position further and possibly set up a time to meet. I was able to reach him on the first try and after speaking with me for several minutes, he arranged for an interview the very next day. I was one of only three candidates selected. The odds sounded more than favorable to me. Thrilled with the prospect of being employed again, I printed out some resumes and did some chores in anticipation of not having free time soon. Optimistically, I rotated my business clothing for the fall to the front of the closet. This job was coming at the perfect time and with only three people in competition, I was as good as employed. Previously, I had banked on retaining my salary until retirement, but had recently started to think it was a pipe dream until this opportunity materialized. When I told Lisa about the job, she said I should be excited but not overly so, and reminded me that I had only a 33% chance of success. She urged me to be positive, not cocky, and to keep my expectations in check.

With my workplace weaknesses being thrown in my face, I was glad the day was over. Always a sound sleeper, for me, the time right before going to sleep was the best for thinking. Even that had changed since I had lost my job. I started dreading going to sleep, tossing and turning all night, while trying to find a way to become relevant again. I hadn't worried about how getting divorced would affect my financial solvency. Never one of those women who had married for money and the trinkets it would bring, I'd always been self-sufficient and proud of it. The fear of not being able to take care of myself for the first time in my life, troubled me enough, that I was determined to nail the interview the following day.

Uncomfortable with test driving a new look, and certain I knew better than Sheila what was appropriate, I dressed in a navy-blue suit and white silk blouse. I had done minimal research on the company and left the house without really giving much thought to their corporate culture. Naively, I expected the interview to go smoothly.

I walked in feeling polished and professional until the receptionist made me doubt myself by looking at me disdainfully as she instructed me to take a seat. A young woman walked in with ankle pants under a neutral silk tunic. She looked self-assured and competent. I walked to the restroom to revisit my wardrobe choice. The reflection I saw in the mirror betrayed me. I looked old and uptight. More than ever, I felt out of place. Einstein had been right after all. He said the meaning of insanity was doing the same thing repeatedly expecting different results. Sheila had drilled it into me differently by saying, "If you always do what you always did, you'll always get what you always got."

I took off my jacket and draped it over my arm in an effort to look more casual when returning to the reception area. When a young man entered the room looking airbrushed and flawless, I lost my confidence all over again. He walked with an easy gait that exuded confidence almost to the point of arrogance. Wearing an eclectic mix of vintage and new garments that others might have thought an odd selection, my competitor appeared to feel confident that he was born to wear his interview outfit. That assuredness was enough for him to pull off the look. To me, he just looked indecisive until he chose the seat next to mine, taking as much space as physically possible for his thin frame while crowding me in. Wanting to unsettle me even more, he asked "Are you legal counsel?"

"No," but before I could ask why, he continued.

"I was trying to find a euphemism for being uptight. Let's just say you look dependable and sturdy, like silverware given as part of a dowry."

The asshole was trying to steal my job by making me feel self-conscious until I decided that we could both play the same game. Trying to sound inquisitive, I asked him "Which of your alter egos is going to interview today, Mr. Park Avenue Uptight or his cousin, the East Village Idiot?" The well-dressed woman stifled a laugh, but stayed above the fray as I tried to reclaim my composure while internally having a meltdown. After eyeing the competition, it looked as though she had already come to the conclusion that the job was hers.

I was the first to be called in. The interviewer wore seersucker pants that were loose fitting with a linen shirt rolled up to his elbows. I was staring at him, trying to figure out if his tan ever faded or came from a bottle, when he asked if I'd come from a funeral. I looked at him inquisitively at first, while trying to recover from the judgmental question. Instead, I complimented him for his keen eye and sixth sense. When he smiled saccharinely, I knew that even if I got the job, we could never work well together. Smart enough to know I had blown it, I stood to leave. The interviewer asked me to sit down. Trying to put me at ease by first saying that my experience was impressive, he proceeded to tell me I probably would not be a good fit. Unable to control myself, I said, "No shit Sherlock. Why don't you clue me in on something I don't already know, like where I went wrong?"

Taken aback by my response, he cocked his head and asked if I really wanted to know. I said yes and he proceeded to. "The world is changing more rapidly than ever before. What you knew yesterday will change by tomorrow. You must get comfortable pivoting on a moment's notice and become fluent in the new technologies. You have to brush up on the new business etiquette." He stood asking me to follow him if I really wanted his advice for acing future interviews. We walked into a large cavernous room with standing desks. Balance balls were the only things that could be used as chairs. The employees were all wearing headsets. "This is how we work. We've done away with email because it is too slow and replaced it with instant messaging. It's working well." I must have looked mortified when he asked if I need to sit down. I thought it a good idea with so many different concepts coming at me. Sitting on a balance ball, proud of myself for not having fallen on my ass, I thanked him for the input. Not wanting to impose by taking any more of his time, I stood to leave. He said, "Julia, you have all the right stuff. You just need to work on how you are presenting it. Believing your own press makes it so."

I let myself out and wished the other candidates better luck. Feeling like a fossilized idiot for not seriously considering the advice I'd been given previously, I dialed Ruth to ask for her help shopping. She agreed and we planned to meet for lunch and a shopping trip the very next day. I went home to register for a couple of classes I had been considering. After a tough morning, I wanted to feel appreciated and walked to Family Friends, where Lynne greeted me with open arms.

"Thank God you are here. We have five new dogs coming in today. I could really use your help. Sarabelle gets unhinged when other dogs come in. Maybe you can play with her while I get the new ones settled. Hey, you look great, but you should really change because they may be a messy bunch and we have lots to do here. I have scrubs from the hospital in the back. Why don't you wear them?"

"Lynne, you don't know how comforting it feels to be useful today."

"Sure I do."

"No, I mean I need to feel positive about something today. I had a miserable day."

"Me too – I lost a newborn baby at work," she said putting it all in perspective.

I changed into the scrubs as Lynne suggested and got ready to help. The dogs came in shortly thereafter, one looking more scared than the next. Each endearing in its own way, I fell in love with three of them instantly. Lynne and I both welcomed our guests appreciatively, thankful for the distraction from life. On days when life had its way with you, it was best to accept the unacceptable and move on.

Just before we locked up for the night, a guy came in with an enormous dog. He introduced himself as Jack, saying he was a city pound employee, and the silver blue Great Dane as Molly. Jack proceeded to tell us her history. She was passed off as a guard dog and thrown in as part of a junkyard deal to a scrap metal dealer. Though she certainly looked imposing, after a few days, her new owner saw that the only damage she could inflict would be licking someone to death. He kept her for a short while, but said she was a nuisance and ate like a horse. He quickly got tired of the responsibility and the expense of feeding her. Not wanting to bother with it, he dropped her off at the pound.

Jack said, "Hoping to dissuade him, we told him that a massive dog like Molly had no chance there and would have to be put down. He turned his back without answering us and walked away abandoning her. We were supposed to put her down within seventy-two hours, but kept Molly for over a month hoping someone might take her because she was a purebred. A buddy of mine watched over her during the day shift and I did at night. Last Monday, the district manager gave us until Saturday morning to get rid of her, or he would put her down himself."

That night, he was supposed to put her down and couldn't bring himself to do it. Jack's building didn't allow pets, so he couldn't even house her temporarily. He had run out of choices until he remembered a flyer he had received from us - my flyer. Before he started his shift, he brought her to Family Friends.

Molly's was extremely timid, afraid of loud noises, and shied away from being touched. Jack told us he thought Molly was about seven years old, my comrade in human years. For a big dog, especially a Great Dane, she was old. In addition to a few visible scars, she had some difficulty getting around. It appeared her joints were achy but some of that was to be expected because of her age. I wondered if she would ever recover from the pain of being abandoned and learn to trust again. Molly winced a little when she got up and walked over to an empty crate, apparently resigned to being caged. A volunteer who had worked at another shelter said she would spend the rest of her life here because of her size and the fact that she was already past her prime. Lynne shot her a look that would freeze a bowl of soup right off the stove, then thanked Jack for bringing her in and saving her life.

It broke my heart to look into her hopeless eyes. Molly was surviving instead of thriving and it looked like she was taking one step in front of the other, just trying to make it through until things got better. I understood her immediately. I decided she was my new housemate and put a collar around her neck at the end of the night. My apartment was small but at least there, Molly could get some rest in a quiet place. She seemed to know instinctively that we were going to be buddies when we stopped at the pet store on the way home. I picked up some food and a couple of toys, though I thought she was probably too old to play with them. I reprimanded myself for passing judgment on her because of age. I hated it when people stereotyped me, but at least, I had not done it maliciously. It was just my assumption based on the visible facts.

Molly was dragging by the time we approached the house. It seemed she wasn't used to getting much exercise after having been caged and the walk might have been too long. She had difficulty negotiating the stairs, but being a willful old girl, she hobbled up them without help. When we arrived at the threshold of what she already seemed to sense was her new home, she wagged her tail vigorously. I opened the door and Molly made her size known by knocking over the only porcelain statue in the place. It had belonged to my mother and was now shattered as part of her grand entrance. Not a great start, but I tried to convince myself that good things take time. Once inside, I gave her water. She happily slopped it up, making a mess of the kitchen floor. I offered her food as well, but she didn't want it. Ten minutes in, the kitchen was a mess, there was a shattered Lladro in the foyer, and a picky dog in the kitchen.

Both exhausted with putting up appearances, still uncomfortable around each other, she sat on the floor and I on the couch not knowing what to do. My new room-mate invited herself up to join me. When scolded and told to get down, she furrowed her brow, but complied begrudgingly. I realized she was going to be a challenge, but it was too late to do anything about it. Even though she looked quite trim, Molly weighed almost 100 pounds and took up the better part of every room in my small apartment. We stared at one another in a way that wasn't confrontational; I, unused to having someone else in my house and she, getting acclimated to her new environment. We both sighed.

She paced through the better part of the long night, unable to settle down or feel comfortable. I had arranged for a visit to the vet the next morning as Lynne suggested. Molly wasn't allowed on the subway or bus, so we walked the twenty blocks to the appointment. While examining her, the vet mentioned that her skin was really dry and her eyes weren't as bright as they should have been. He noted that at a hundred pounds, she was underweight for her size. There was some inflammation in her joints and he suggested that I keep the walks short at first, then slowly increase the distance as her condition improved.

"Ok. Oh, I almost forgot to tell you she didn't eat last night."

"Good. The best thing you can do for her right now is to see how she reacts when she has a clean slate. Nothing but boiled chicken, sweet potatoes, and plain rice for the next week. Bring her back after that and we'll see how Molly is doing."

When we got home, she continued her anxious pacing. Although I was not comfortable doing it, I left her home alone and went to meet Ruth for an afternoon of lunch and shopping. It was good to catch up with my friend again. It took her about a minute to ask what classes I was taking and how I was managing with all the free time. There really wasn't much down time. I told her about signing up for technology classes after my last interview and also about volunteering. Now that Molly was with me, there would be even less free time.

Ruth and I walked towards the east side to shop in New York's premium stores. I really didn't know my way around the shops I had always thought of as the native habitat for upper east siders. The stores, like their inhabitants were stuffy, overpriced, and uninteresting. Even the sales clerks had attitude. They weren't like the ones at Saks, who knew that the wealthiest of the bunch didn't have to try to look it. The establishments oozed fashionistas that reeked of nouveau rich, wannabe money.

Eventually, not finding what we wanted, we made our way farther uptown. Ruth said she was looking for something that would make me look like I wasn't a virgin in casual business apparel. I was totally lost and had no idea what she meant. Business apparel had always been like a uniform to me - predictable, uninspiring, and nondescript. Athleisure was more my style. I loved a good pair of sneakers, yoga pants, and a fun top, but here, in the valley of suede slacks and cashmere sweaters sets, I was out of my element.

Ruth was dressed elegantly and looked as though she'd worn the perfect outfit to go anywhere.

"I'm so glad my guardian angel swooped down to help me. I would be lost without you."

"I'm just excited that you've finally decided to get clothes that reflect who you really are Julia. Let's go, this is not the right department for you."

Within the maze of racks, Ruth effortlessly steered me towards the jewel-toned sportswear and selected an outfit. With fall upon us, the weather would be turning soon. She picked a pumpkin-colored cashmere jacket, brown suede leggings, and a fitted lightweight knit crewneck sweater. The outfit appeared to be perfect for the look I wanted to convey.

"There you go. Smart, casual, fashionable and elegant. Breakfast of champions."

"How'd you do that?"

"I know you, Julia. Clothes are only an expression of who you are. Now for shoes."

We walked to the shoe department where I tried on loafers, driver mocs, booties, and flats. It wasn't until we found a pair of soft, tumbled leather monk straps that I felt comfortable. When I put them on, we both knew they were right.

"Do you have a bag?" she asked.

"Of course."

"No Julia, I mean a BAG. One that says I've arrived without being too flashy. A great bag is a good investment."

"You mean like this one?" I asked holding up what to me looked like a stylish designer handbag.

"No dear. Not one that says 'and I came by bus'. Ah, here we go. Beautiful, understated, obviously of the best quality, without a logo and made in Italy. Just what the doctor ordered and it's now only $280."

"Gulp," I said out loud.

"And my gift to you – all of it," she said as we approached the register.

"I can't let you do that. I will put it on my card. I'm not destitute yet."

"Nonsense Julia. This is not a pity gift. Nothing would give me more pleasure than to buy you the outfit that lands you a great job." Her generosity was as genuine as her laughter and I was humbled by her friendship. She picked up a pair of socks from the impulse queue and without asking, dropped them on the counter beside the rest of my goodies.

"Ruth. How do I begin to thank you?"

"Get a job that is rewarding and learn to be happy!"

That evening, I cooked for myself the same thing that Molly needed to be fed and sat down to my bland dinner with a glass of wine. I set her bowl down as well. She approached it, breathing in deeply, waiting to be reprimanded. Then, she finally tasted the food and looked at me questioningly, going back to the food at least three or four times as though waiting to hear no. When she realized that she was not going to be scolded, Molly made a kind of growling, happy noise and proceeded to savor every morsel, as though it were her last meal. It saddened me to think that it might have been had Jack not brought her to us.

At night, I struggled to get her down the stairs. She didn't want to leave the house, but once forced to go outside, she marked the sidewalk the way a male dog would have, staking her claim. She was restless until we got back home. Back inside, Molly finally settled in.

The next few days were almost mirror images of one another. She was timid, but when I moved from room to room, she followed, not wanting to lose sight of me. When I needed to run an errand, Molly stood by my side. It was clear she was waiting to be invited for the outing and more often than not, I didn't have the heart to turn her down.

Though she was a big responsibility and had made my couch a giant chew toy within the first few days, I liked having her around. The guy at the deli did also and would let me come in with Molly when the store was empty. At the cheese store, the owner always gave her a chunk of Gouda. I started to notice that people related differently to me because of her. Molly was quite the ice breaker and when I was with her, I was a quieter, gentler version of myself. I was more patient with her than I had ever been and found she brought out the best in me. From the start, she was great company and became my confidante, always willing to lend an ear.

One of her favorite adventures was doing laundry. Molly always came along and what used to be a chore, was now fun. It became a time for us to bond. I hated going into the basement of the building alone and she loved being with me. Even without my undivided attention there, she was still part of the action. Her listless gaze was gone. Her body became stronger from our walks and her mind was stimulated by the new sights and smells. Her entire demeanor was changing. Lynne explained it easily by saying that since she had a special someone in her life, she had something to live for.

I had become comfortable with my routine, but knew that soon, it would have to come to an end. I needed income and searched the job sites constantly. Disappointed with the options offered, I found that several postings were being recycled. Had the hires been let go or were the ads just window dressing to draw traffic to the site? I remembered Sheila saying many employers were given incentives to keep the positions up longer than they needed to be. Some even remained after the jobs had been filled to show lots of opportunities. All the hype about the economy picking up was just that. Many of the people I knew without jobs had thrown their hands up and even stopped looking. The "new normal", as the political pundits like to call it, sucked.

Wanting a distraction from my financial nightmare, I could think of no better way than helping at Family Friends. It was physically demanding work to care for the dogs, but it was rewarding. When I volunteered, I always took Molly with me. Lynne appointed her the greeter for people who came in looking to adopt. By that time, she was very friendly and a splendid example of how even the biggest dogs make great pets regardless of how small your space is. We had about a dozen dogs who all needed attention and together, we handled everything, accomplishing a great deal. It was rewarding to see how many dogs were being adopted and to be part of something worthwhile that was becoming successful. It reminded me of just how much I had hated working for Michael.

Lynne and I sat for a cup of coffee just before we closed up shop. She looked apprehensive, then said, "What the hell. What's the worst that can happen? You turn me down. So what?"

"What do you mean?" I asked.

"The hospital has asked that I work extra hours to train several new nurses. It will mean more money. I could really use it. I've been making up for the shortfall here with my own funds."

"I had no idea. We are busier lately, right? So you won't have to dip into your money anymore."

She nodded, affirming that I was correct.

"I don't understand what your concern is?"

"Well, it's just that I don't want to leave the shelter short-handed. We've gotten local recognition and can start to rescue more dogs. We have enough business to hire someone, but I haven't been able to find the right person."

"What are you looking for?"

"I'm looking for someone responsible, loving, dependable, smart, and caring. I'm looking for you."

"I'm flattered Lynne, thank you. I'll help as much as I can, but I have to find a job."

"Why must you make everything so difficult? Listen to what I'm saying. I'm offering you an interim job.

I'm sure I can't pay close to what you are worth, but I don't have much room on the salary."

"Don't worry. You don't have to pay me anything. I'll keep volunteering until I find something else."

"Instead of having you volunteer, I want to pay you. You could probably use the money and would be a great help to me at the same time. You won't have to be here forty hours, so you will still have time to search for a job in your field. I can pay you twenty-five thousand dollars a year. I hope that's not offensive. Would you consider it?"

"Consider it? I'd love it. I've been going crazy looking for work and can't find anything. I adore working with the dogs. I'll accept the job as long as you know it is just temporary. Are you okay with that?"

"Absolutely. I already said that. This is great – you made my day!"

"Thanks for thinking of me. Your offer really couldn't have come at a better time. When do I start?"

She replied smiling that I already had and that my title was Director of Marketing and Public Relations for Family Friends.

At least now, I had a job. Though it didn't pay what I was used to, it was something I knew I would enjoy. It gave me a place to go and a commitment to honor. I had spent many fruitless hours staring at the computer screen searching for an opening that didn't exist. Not only would this help provide for me financially, it would also shorten the gap between jobs.

With no excuse now that I earned a paycheck, it was time to refocus efforts on my non-existent romantic life. I had already tried the dating sites without any success. They were filled with players, some worse than others. Maybe meeting several guys within the course of a single night was the way to go. Call me crazy, but I wasn't willing to give up until I arrived at Oz and found no wizard. I thought speed-dating might be a good option, and the fact that I did scared me more than a little.

I did some research online to find out which were the best speed-dating events. Madeline said she had gone to one where she met three really nice guys and was now dating one of them exclusively. She gave me the number to call and told me to be sure to reserve my spot. When I spoke with Albert, the event coordinator, he said it would be as easy as picking up a burger at a drive through. Lovely analogy that it was, I eagerly enlisted.

The fateful event took place at a dingy east side neighborhood bar that was only in business because of groups like his. Even getting there was a challenge. It was on the wrong side of Alphabet City and though the neighborhood was changing, it was still considered somewhat sketchy. The locale was dimly lit and in hindsight, that may have been a blessing.

The organizer had aligned twenty-four people, women aged 42 - 54 and men 45 – 57 in a forced social situation that could best be described as a blend between musical chairs and square dancing. The only exception was that no one called out for you to face your partner. Albert was off to a good start with the age groups he had selected. The brackets gave men a three-year edge to address the younger woman thing most of them wanted. It was well thought out. I had to give him credit for planning it this way until he turned up the lights. I had jumped to the wrong conclusion again and it was all downhill from there. Once assembled, the men got progressively worse as my eyes moved down the line from one to the next. The pick of the litter, a more accurate statement than I would have liked to admit, was a shy, nebbish looking guy, who was so amped up that he was loud and boisterous. After the third bachelor, the guys started looking like single room occupancy inhabitants who had just graduated from group therapy. It appeared as though Albert had combed the soup lines for homeless men to recruit the last few.

The women, on the other hand, were well-dressed, impeccably groomed, and looked intelligent enough to carry on a conversation with strangers. At first glance, they appeared to be successful and seemed to be educated. When I overheard them speak, I was impressed with their knowledge of current events, travel, and sports. It was the Graces meet Beowulf.

I was the third grace in the rotation of twelve. I knew it was going to be a long night when my first six-minute date took three minutes to walk several yards to me. Once he arrived, he sat huffing loudly, smiled self-consciously while perspiring, and almost hyperventilated before my eyes.

When he finally caught his breath, he asked, "So, do you live in a one-story house or in an elevator building?"

"Fourth-floor walkup," I replied.

He snorted and said, "Well, I guess I'll never see the inside of your bedroom."

I was taken aback by his assumption. He did not have an ice cube's chance in hell of ever seeing the post office in my neighborhood, much less the inside of my bedroom. Unbelievable!

The second guy seemed okay – at least he could walk. As soon as he sat down, he started his shtick. His claim to fame was that he could recite the Caribbean islands he'd been to alphabetically. I remembered David's advice about being open to new experiences. My enthusiastic willingness to give bachelor number two the benefit of the doubt was my way of showing the universe that I was listening. Even so, the best I could give my mini date was that he liked to travel.

"Antigua, Aruba, Guadalupe, Grenada, Nassau, Paradise Island and St. Martin," he proudly announced.

Afterwards, he sat uncomfortably in silence for a moment, then volunteered the unsolicited tidbit that Nassau was his favorite because he had some company during that trip. He winked and said that he had gone there last year with his mom and Sister Gertrude from her church group.

Way to rock my world buddy! I prayed to Sister Gertrude that the six minutes would come to an end quickly and painlessly. Eager to move on, even the short "dates" were too long. In the hopes that good things were worth waiting for, I called the third customer in the bakery of single life.

An Asian guy approached the table and greeted me with a shy nod and a slight bow. He was so true to the stereotype in appearance, speech, and mannerisms, that I couldn't keep a straight face. Wearing black pants, a white dress shirt and black vest, I wasn't sure if he was there to romance me or take my order. He interpreted my ear to ear grin as a sign that I was interested. My date couldn't have been a day under 65. First, I wondered how he had slipped in past the age cutoff. Then, I marveled at how he did it without getting carded when he wasn't an inch over five feet tall. It amazed me how long the six-minute race lasted for this jockey whose speech was very deliberate and painfully slow. I was certain that my eyes had glazed over and thought the horse must have broken his leg, forcing this guy to walk the final stretch to the finish line. I celebrated the small victory of having survived the race and welcomed the leave of absence an upcoming bathroom break would provide.

The organizer deserved credit for realizing who his audience was - middle aged women who couldn't make it through a movie without having to pee. Doctors say that it's the hormones that cause this phenomenon to occur on your 45th birthday, but I think it is a self-serving ritual. A weak bladder allows the single older woman a reprieve from her very boring dinner companion. Thinking of it as a stay of execution, granted by a charitable governor, I walked/ran to the bathroom chuckling the entire way.

Seeing my life play out as though I were watching a film unnerved me. What happened to survival of the fittest in this new-age dating ritual? Apparently, Darwin had taken a wrong turn somewhere, and we had ended up in this makeshift freak show called dating in your 40's, which was not to be confused with sleeping around in your 30's, or settling in your 50's. Acting as though there were really suitable partners out there, I put up a front and it seemed the others were doing the same. I knew better, honest to God, but along with the other women waiting for one of the two stalls, I went through the motions with an engaging smile and generally good spirits. As it turned out, the most success any of us felt we had that night was meeting a bunch of great women who we would enjoy hanging out with again. The sisterhood felt like a sorority which men were pledging. We put them through the paces and the victor for the evening was the organizer himself. Looking back on it, I'm certain Albert was playing out his mommy fantasies. In his late 30's, not bad looking and not really employed, he sat on the sidelines waiting for one of the women to be disappointed because she was going home alone. He'd be there, ready to fill in, by easing the pain of loneliness. After all, there was nothing like settling for being part of a loser's fantasy to lift a gal's spirits after a long, uneventful night.

I braced myself as I left the sanctuary of the bathroom to face the barbarians again. The least offensive in the group was being snatched up (open to your interpretation) by a woman so sick of buying her vibrator batteries at Costco that anything was an improvement.

When I told Lisa about my evening, she asked me to reconsider meeting Joshua. Joey had been trying to fix me up for some time with a friend of his and I agreed to give it some thought. She sent me his picture from a company party. I had to admit he was not bad looking and finally accepted an invitation to meet him Friday night. They were having three couples over for a few cocktails. It wouldn't feel so awkward with other people I knew there. Lisa might have resurrected him after a rant about my lack of purpose and passionless existence since losing my job.

Joshua "looked good on paper" but turned out to be a dud. Meeting him at Lisa's gathering was about as stimulating as drinking lukewarm tea when you were sick and couldn't taste or even smell anything. There wasn't anything special about him, but nothing was really wrong with him either. With that resounding endorsement, Joshua became my next foray into the dating circuit. He was a 50-year-old contractor and in retrospect, we should have been perfect for each other. He was boring and I was bored to death. He lived his life like he ran his business, always analyzing the numbers and budgeting to cut corners. Call me crazy, but the last thing you wanted while on a date was to see the odds as a guy mentally calculated, his eyes tallying left and right, the probability of whether or not he was going to bag you that evening.

You could say he was handsome in the conventional sense. No woman would kick him out of bed for eating crackers. However, I imagined that once he got there, the crackers would be the best part of the meal. He was as sensual as a brick, but dependable, predictable, loyal and hardworking. Maybe I was asking too much. After the second date, when he still hadn't kissed me, I asked him why. He responded by telling me he never kissed until after the third date. Who was this guy, Doris Day? Well, on the fourth date, I was sorry I ever asked. Perhaps it was normal to feel like you were being prodded by aliens while you were being kissed. If that was the trailer, the main event was sure to be a horror flick. In my mind, the movie would play out something like this: A somewhat attractive, middle-aged woman, who looked like a heavier version of Winona Ryder's mother, saunters into a dimly lit bedroom where Romeo awaits her under the covers. They begin kissing and then WHAM – his titanium member methodically rises like the queen alien ready to pierce her as soon as the opportunity presents itself. It could have potential as a groundbreaking new genre - Romantic Horror Comedy. The bedroom scenes would be challenging, but if massaged properly, they could reach new heights of laughing all the way to the bed. From there, it would just drag on and on. The movie critic in my mind was convinced that most women would fall asleep before the closing credits.

After a handful of dates, I sensed that with Joshua, there wouldn't be a lot of drama. That was a good thing. It was the reason that was the problem. I wasn't emotionally invested and he was totally incapable of ever being so. At least it was comforting to know that when we broke up, nobody's feelings would get hurt. Playing it safe sounded like a viable option. I was being practical and not rolling over to show my jugular for once. My history with Alan was plagued with bad decisions made by my heart. The Matthew fiasco ushered in more of the same. Since then, trying to deflect more heartbreak, I was over-thinking things and by doing so, screwing it all up. My attitude towards romance could have been compared to wearing sensible shoes. I sacrificed what I wanted for what was practical, and ended up compromising the right look and feel, for what made sense.

Sandwiched in between random disheartening interviews, on weekends Joshua and I typically went to see a movie. The flick, always his pick, was usually selected because it had been touted as the biggest box office draw. Afterwards, we would stop for a slice and then say goodbye at the subway stop, each going our own way at the end of the evening. It wasn't exciting, but it was nice to have the company. I needed something to help lift my spirits since the interviews were not panning out, but he wasn't it.

Even when we were together, I still felt lonely. Work had always provided interaction with other people and though I'd always considered myself a solitary person, I missed having that. With Joshua in the picture, I was seeing some current flicks and was able to talk about the news. It wasn't all bad and only became a little tense each time the bill arrived. He would pull out his phone to calculate exactly how much to tip. Twice, we'd actually tried to bounce ideas off each other but neither of us seemed to value the input given, so our most meaningful conversations were about whether the waiter deserved fifteen or eighteen percent. Joshua always seemed to settle on twelve. Maybe he wasn't even that good with numbers.

I convinced myself that falling in love as a middle-aged woman was different and we continued to date. My justification was that at this age, it wasn't possible to fall in love. Maybe, now it was just something you stepped into gingerly. I questioned whether my point of reference was all wrong. I still wanted my heartbeat to accelerate at the thought of seeing him and longed for the days before caller ID, when you had to wait to see if it was him on the other end of the line. There had to be a man out there who could wake my heart up and excite me both mentally and physically, or was that territory reserved only for teenage girls and rom-coms?

After questioning whether or not romance existed, I checked my email to find a message from a Match subscriber. He said that I looked familiar, maybe from Perfect Fitness, and wanted to meet. Maybe the gym would be my ticket to paradise after all.

I thought about the offer for a minute or two, then decided to take the plunge. What the hell did I have to lose? Joshua wasn't for me and I wasn't willing to settle for a mediocre relationship after shopping for so long. I found the new guy's profile online and still did not recognize him, but I replied to my mysterious liaison anyway asking if he had time for a cup of coffee today. He answered me instantly, suggesting the Starbucks on 82nd and Broadway as a possible rendezvous spot. It was Isaac's location and that alone should have been the harbinger of another foiled romance, but I agreed to meet him anyway. When asked how I'd know who he has, his response was that he would be wearing a Harris Tweed jacket and he knew who I was. Before signing off, he added that oh by the way, his name was Mark.

When I walked in, Isaac flagged me over. "Couldn't stay away huh, back for more fun? It's okay, I'll accept your apology if you get a doctor's note," he said pointing towards the corner.

Without giving him the courtesy of a response, I scanned the room until my eyes settled on a guy wearing a sports jacket with his back to me. It was the guy Isaac had pointed to. I walked towards him, hoping for sparks, until I got closer and recognized him. It was the guy from the gym who carried his own disinfectant wipes. When he saw me, he stood and gave me a very far apart hug that felt more like the start of a pat down at airport security than it did an embrace. Great, a germaphobe!

"Hi, I'm Mark. So nice to meet you."

"Likewise. I'm Julie, Thanks for reaching out."

"How do you like your coffee?"

"Tall and strong," I had to fight back the urge to say it, but he completed the sentence for me.

"Like your men?"

I smiled thinking that at least he had a sense of humor and that was not a bad place to start.

He returned with our beverages, then proceeded to carefully prepare his for consumption by scrubbing it down with an antibacterial wipe, while holding a napkin near the rim where his lips would touch the lid. Placing his cup on the table as though he had not just done something super weird, he started a casual conversation. By the time Mark finished a half cup of coffee, he had moved us to the couch, where he began psycho-analyzing me. He asked where I'd grown up, what my parents did for a living and how many siblings I had. Mark continued grilling me by asking where I was in the birth order and by the rapid-fire sound of it, he was just warming up. Next, he asked me to write a sentence on the napkin, handing me his Waterman pen in a plastic sleeve reminiscent of a rubber, so my nasty hand wouldn't infect his instrument. Lovely. When I asked why he wanted me to write something, he explained that before dating someone, he always analyzed her handwriting to determine if she was a woman of character or not. What a crock of shit! Put off by his request, at first, I paused, then with nothing to lose, decided play along. As I started writing, I wondered why I agreed to be tested on a first date and it struck me as funny. I paused for a moment thinking of something clever to write. Putting pen to paper, I decided to write *I am not contagious, except of course, for a handful of sexually transmitted diseases.* As soon as I had started scribing my second sentence, I realized that Mark had stood up and without further explanation, said he had to be going and would see me at the gym.

Compelled to learn what the turn off had been, I asked why he was leaving. He proceeded to tell me that it was clear I was impulsive, not open-minded enough, had loose morals, and was somewhat stubborn because I was left-handed. His analysis was not bad actually and I suggested he take it up as a profession. I laughed thinking he was kidding until he asked for his pen back. As I held it out to him, he retrieved it by grasping the end, away from where my hand had touched it, and then carefully sliding the pen out of its plastic protector. Mark, who left me holding the empty sleeve, looked at me disgustedly. Amused with the whole situation, I grabbed him by the shoulders and the shock of it forced his mouth open in a silent scream. I gave him a big, sloppy open-mouthed kiss to seal the deal. He became so phobic that I thought he would faint, but he just ran out instead. Isaac couldn't miss a single chance to jab me. He sprinted to my table and under the guise of wiping it down asked, "Is it safe to approach the quarantined area? Another one bites the dust Resuscitation Sally. Must be your pheromones."

At the moment, my professional life was as unsuccessful as my romantic one. I'd been on four interviews over the last several weeks, felt that three had gone well, and was expecting a callback from at least a couple of them. Though I sent follow up emails, no responses came. When I didn't get them, the little confidence I struggled to retain, melted away.

The internet had created a glut of candidates for any open position, professional or romantic. I found myself in a large candidate pool where there was always someone who was a better fit, younger or cheaper. Sheila offered some suggestions to help differentiate me from the masses. She was right again. My resume was good but it needed to be great. It was non-descript, didn't express my personality, and was safe, just like my profile had been. Maybe I was presenting myself as someone complacent who would be okay with mediocrity. I expressed my concerns and she listened, nodding her agreement. The department offered a single session with a life coach as part of the outplacement program and she thought it merited my consideration. I had always felt that New Yorkers were too quick to jump on the therapist's couch, but my methods weren't working and the price was right. The coach also came recommended by someone who I trusted, so it was worth a shot.

The glorified cheerleader's office was in the West Village. Perfect, a flaky neighborhood for my quack doctor. The guru's shingle read 'Success Creator' paving the way for more doubts about the whole process. When Toni stepped out of her office wearing a flowing skirt, a garnet colored mala, and a charismatic smile, I was a little surprised that she, appeared to have been a he, in her prior life. Amused that my coach did not come with original equipment, but had an impressive after assembly rack, probably a newly revamped glove compartment and a welcoming smile, I started to feel confident that she could help with my transformation as well. Toni hugged me hello with a little too much vigor and greeted me by saying that I should make myself comfortable. I was thankful that the office didn't have a couch in it. The furniture consisted of a glass desk and a balance ball for her. For me, it offered the choice of a rocking chair, a barstool, a tufted leather seat, or some cushy, large pillows strewn around the floor. I knew it was a test, so I sat in the tufted leather chair and asked her if I passed. Looking puzzled, she replied, "If you passed what?" When I told her that I wanted to know if I had passed the seating test, she laughed and asked, "Are you always so skeptical?" I thought about it and replied with latent anger that, yes, I was, especially since I didn't know whether to refer to her as sir or madam. "Just call me Toni and we'll be fine," she replied without batting an eye.

We spoke for the hour, getting to know each other. The whole process was not as intrusive as I feared it would be. Taking notes as we spoke, when our time was up, she asked if I wanted her professional evaluation. I did. After telling me that I was closed off to possibilities, she recommended developing a more accepting approach to life in general and said that when a person was not open to the opportunities, nothing would present itself. Then Toni told me how it was only when she gave herself permission to dream about her future that she admitted to being born in the wrong body. Toni explored her options and came to understand that the exterior unit had to be replaced and repurposed for in-house. Trying to be funny, I told her that it was not the first time I'd heard that. My contractor had suggested the same thing almost verbatim when I had expanded my cape years ago. Disregarding my sarcasm, Toni said that it was clear from the start of our conversation what my issues were. She asked me to practice an exercise for the next week. I was supposed to trust my instincts and question things only when there was a conflict between the visible facts and what I was being told. I had to trust until I was given reason not to. She might as well have asked me to beam a man up to the moon using a laser pointer, but I told her I'd try. She committed to following up with Sheila to see how I was doing. Before parting, I asked if she would be willing to answer a personal question.

"It would be my pleasure to answer anything as honestly as possible."

I asked, "Is sex was more pleasurable as a man or a woman?"

Toni thought about it and laughed a long, hearty laugh. After a moment, she said, "Honey, it doesn't matter whether you pitch or catch as long as you are in the game, you like the feel of having bats and balls in hand, and are cordial to the other team."

After my session with Toni, I decided not to sit through another movie with Joshua. I spoke with Lisa and found myself spitting out, less than diplomatically, that he just didn't do it for me. Lisa understood and asked why it had taken me so long to share my feelings. I couldn't answer because I really didn't know. Maybe I was trying to accept that someone like Joshua was really all that was available to me at this point in my life, but then changed my mind.

Lisa had already moved on and told me about a singles group she had heard advertised on the radio the day before. The events sounded like they could be fun, so I signed up for Meet Market Adventures after we hung up. The group was created by a hipster named Clay, who supposedly knew every hotspot in the tristate area.

Their next event was being held in a trendy bar in Nolita. I recruited Audra, one of the women I'd met speed dating to join me for the adventure. Nate drove us there and arranged to pick us up at 11:59 p.m. or as he put it, before we turned into pumpkins.

The bar was overcrowded and noisy. The expensive venue was rife with hipsters and hipsters in training. Perfect! So as the group started assembling, I noticed the men, who were our age or older, were all puffing out their chests for the 30-year-olds. Apparently, the pigeons thought this courting dance might make them attractive to someone premenopausal. Shit, that was wishful thinking. They were not even attractive to us and let's face it, Audra and I were not the most discriminating consumers at this point.

We had a drink while deciding whether or not to sit back and watch the show. The newbie women in the group were trying. God love them, they were really trying, but still didn't realize that a few things were out of place. First of all, the dimples on their thighs should have been either on their cheeks or just above their other cheeks. Their breasts were pendulous rather than perky. Another strike against them was that these women could hold a conversation about something other than the man talking. What sealed their fate, however, was that they actually had opinions and were able to share them. They had no chance against the Ms. Nod-it-All's who'd smile at the middle-aged wallets willing to buy the drinks for the night. So, the 50-year-old guys would ply the 30-year-old hotties with cocktails in the hopes that by the end of the night they'd look good enough to eat. What actually happened was that after the last call, the 30-year-old hipsters made off with the spoils without spending a penny on the women. The old guys had done the heavy lifting and now were being taken off the field to make room for the closers. Perfect night for the hipsters, free pussy for them without the work or the expense. The old guys limped back to the locker room with Viagra induced hard-ons slowing their progress. It was a hoot to watch, but other than the voyeurism, the night was a complete bust. Audra was exhausted and took the first cab she saw home. I was wired and after calling Nate to cancel, decided to walk back. Exhausted from the effort of trying to be social, I was tired of playing the game. Maybe Nate had been right and it was time to hang up my heels and switch to sensible shoes instead.

Singles events could be depressing at times. It was easy to become almost oblivious to the surroundings and people, going by rote through the sea of faces, all nondescript, all looking for something or someone to make the pain go away. Though the venues changed, one event was barely distinguishable from the next. The evening had been like many before it, but Audra's company had helped, or maybe it was me. Lately, even if things did not work out as expected, I still found a way to have fun. I admit that sometimes it was at another's expense, but rationalized that since the person didn't know, no harm was done.

It felt as though if I could get through this, something better would surface on the other side. It wasn't until after I had crossed 14th Street that my feet started barking. Having hoofed a mile in heels, I took my delayed anguish in the fashionable footwear as a sign that I was well-equipped to stay in the game and win it. I think it was Robert Frost who first said that "the best way out was always through". Maybe he was on to something. How's that for an open mind?

CHAPTER 10

PAUL

When I got home, my answering machine was flashing incessantly. The message counter showed that three messages had been received. Without listening to them, I changed into comfy pajamas and went to bed. In the morning, before even brushing my teeth, I went directly to the machine and played them back. One was from Nate, reminding me that Frank was in town the following week and we were all going to dinner. I went on to the next message flicking away the previous voicemail like an annoying mosquito.

The second was from a guy named Paul. He started the message by saying that we'd met a few months back during First Night at the Rose Planetarium and I had given him my number. He had not called because he was trying to work things out with his girlfriend before finalizing their decision to part ways. He had kept my number in the possible follow-up file for a couple of months and said I'd been on his mind a few times since then. When it was clear they had no future, he reached out. I couldn't place him or remember any conversation from that night, but was flattered that I had made a memorable impression. Quickly jotting down his number before listening to the last message, I was excited, in spite of the fact that I didn't know who he was. The last message was from Ruth. She was heading west on a last-minute trip to see Luke. She didn't say much else, other than that he needed her help with something.

I stared at the phone, playing referee between logic and desire, not wanting to appear desperate, to determine how long I'd wait to call Paul. It was only eight in the morning. I talked myself into waiting until at least ten. Since he didn't know I just received the message, it would be ok to call early. I went to the gym and by the time I got home to shower, it was already almost H hour.

While still in my bathrobe, with towel-dried hair, I made the call and he picked up on the first ring.

"Hi Paul. This is Julia."

"Julia," he completed my name a little too excitedly. His voice was smooth and sensuously deep. He sounded erotic, maybe even dangerous, and for me, that was a headily, intoxicating mix.

"Hi," I said reclaiming my composure. "I got your message, but to be perfectly candid, I don't remember exactly who you are."

"Of course not," he said. "I didn't think you would. A successful woman like you must have a great deal on her mind."

"How'd you know I'd call you back then?" I asked, curious to hear his response.

"I didn't, but it was worth a try. I'm so glad you were intrigued enough to follow up. When we met, you said you were a Yankees fan, so you will understand that because you called back, 'today I consider myself the luckiest man in the world.'"

Ok. This guy had done this before. That much was clear from his confident, smooth delivery. I didn't care. I liked what he was selling and he knew it. We had an animated, intelligent conversation. It was refreshing to hear someone speak, who was living

225

proof that there was civilized life on the planet after all. After spending about a half hour on the phone, Paul asked if I would have a drink with him.

"I'd really like that, however, I am very busy this week with a new job," I said postponing the meeting without being sure why I'd done it.

"Not a problem. I'm travelling until Wednesday the following week, so let's firm up plans now. I'm thinking maybe we could meet at Michael's Pub a week from Thursday."

I would have agreed with the plan had I been given a chance to. Not impressed with his solo decision, yet trying to brush it off, I responded, "Hey, do you know if Woody Allen still plays there after his bad press?"

"I'm not sure, but why wouldn't he? People make mistakes. He shouldn't be blacklisted for having made one in his personal life," Paul said. He sounded reasonable although I didn't agree with his opinion, until he added, "I'll see you Thursday at seven. Don't be late." Then trying to soften the command he added, "Because they won't let people in between sets. Good luck with the job. I know you'll wow them just like you did me."

After I hung up, the phone rang immediately. I thought Paul had forgotten to tell me something, so I picked up and said, "I always do that too."

"What are you talking about?" Nate asked sounding confused.

"Oh, hey there. I'm sorry. I thought you were Paul."

"Who's Paul? Never mind, you'll fill me in when I see you. Maureen and I would like you to join us for a night out. Frank will be in town and that way you two can meet - no pressure."

"I don't know. I'm kind of tired," I replied trying to dissuade him from insisting any further.

"Bullshit. You haven't even heard when we are going and besides, you have all week to rest. We are picking you up for dinner on Friday at 8:00 p.m. We'll go someplace for great Italian."

Seemed like dominant men were the order of the day. Twice in a matter of minutes, I had been told what to do. If Nate had opened with great Italian, I would have accepted without an argument. It sounded yummy. Even if Frank was a dud, the food would be good. Besides, I liked their company and it had been awhile since I'd seen Nate. Meeting someone through friends would be a welcome change from chatting up a stranger in a forced social situation. Despite my best efforts, there was no special man in my life and with only Paul on the horizon, keeping my options open was a good idea. We hadn't been on a date yet, and though he had potential, he also appeared to be a little intense. Juggling a couple of men in the circus of single life might be fun for a change. "Okay," I reconsidered, still unfamiliar with the rules that were in play with my new open-door policy. "That sounds great."

I looked outside and decided to open the windows and let some fresh air in. The brilliant sun shone through the drapes. The air was crisp and cool. Even the trees had brought out their finery and were resplendent in vibrant, jewel-toned colors. It was a perfect fall day. I found myself humming as I moved between chores, bouncing from one to the next in a volley. I couldn't remember ever whistling or humming before, but lately, I had caught myself doing just that several times. Even with nothing exceptional going on, I was enjoying life.

I cleaned up the apartment and by six o'clock, the place was immaculate. I had completed my chores and was looking forward to my dinner date. And yes, I had to admit to being excited about meeting Frank as well. Wouldn't it be funny if he turned out to be the one? True to form, Molly was waiting as I stepped out of the shower. She was always happy to be around me and I had grown accustomed to having her as my shadow. I wondered whether she was part of the catalyst for my happy outlook. Putting on some makeup in an effort to look natural but younger, I opted to wear my hair up. After all, face lift and uplift were both good things. They pointed to an upward trajectory, so an up-do might be a stealthy way to cheat the evil Sorceress Gravity as well.

At 8:00 p.m. sharp, I went downstairs feeling fairly confident that my outfit looked good and laughed when I thought about how pleased Punctual Paul would be with my precision timing. When I stepped into their car Maureen said, "Julie, you smell great. What are you wearing?"

"Prada," I said, happy that she appreciated the beautiful fragrance. I hoped that Nate had remembered to purchase some perfume for her and made a mental note to ask him next time we spoke. After all, nothing can make a woman feel sexier than a great perfume.

Nate turned around and remarked "Wow. You're a knockout."

I smiled at both of them, "Thanks, guys. That helps. I despise first dates. Where is he anyway? I figured he'd be in the car."

"He's meeting us at the restaurant. We were supposed to pick him up at the hotel but he landed late, so he's meeting us at Don Pep's. It's easy to get there from JFK and they have the best Milanese this side of Italy.

Maureen added, "The atmosphere at the restaurant leaves a little to be desired, but the food is great and it's casual, so I thought it would be a good spot to make it feel less orchestrated. Hey, Nate tells me there may already be a new guy on the horizon."

"Well, hopefully. We only met once several months ago and haven't really dated yet, but he's got a great voice. Anyway, his name is Paul and we just reconnected. He seems a little domineering, but to tell you the truth, it kind of gives me a cheap thrill to have someone take control. Even on the phone though, he's a little overbearing in a creepy kind of way."

"Now, there's a ringing endorsement! All kidding aside, be careful if you feel that way. You can't go out with every weirdo who whispers the things you want to hear," Nate said in a fatherly voice.

"I'm going to hate seeing him when Mery starts to date, but this time, Nate's right." Turning to her husband, Maureen said, "Promise me you won't let it go to your head honey, even a blind squirrel finds a nut occasionally. Seriously Julie, it's the guys who tell you the things you don't want to hear that are the keepers."

I thought about what Maureen said in silence for a few moments and surmised that she was right. We crossed over to Queens via the midtown tunnel, and were surprised to see that one tube had been completely closed off to incoming traffic. It made the road in the opposite direction a parking lot. Luckily, we didn't hit a snag and made it through in no time.

"I bet at least a third of those people are missing a show," I said pointing to the oncoming traffic.

"I figured there wouldn't be traffic Queens bound, but sometimes, it is better to be lucky than smart," Nate replied. Maureen looked at him raising her eyebrows. It was clear from her reaction that it had not been his idea.

We arrived at the restaurant and found a parking spot right in front. The place wasn't much to look at, but the line out the door reinforced Nate's rave review. When I asked how they had discovered the place, he jumped on the question to tell me the story. "As newlyweds, we lived in Howard Beach in a basement studio right around the corner. We had both recently graduated and were living on peanuts. Maureen and I saved every penny of disposable income to go on one great date a month and ended up always coming here. We usually didn't have the room or the money for dessert, but it made no difference. We still had a blast. The owner, who had become friendly with us, and gotten in the habit of packing up two cannoli on the house for us to take home. He usually presented them along with the check. It wasn't until years later that he told us why he did it. He had noticed how carefully we counted our money and knew we were strapped. The cannoli were his way of contributing to the cause."

Maureen added, "Coming here always brings back great memories. We were so happy, even then. It doesn't matter what you don't have, if you have a great partner, you are rich."

Realizing it was a difficult subject for me, Nate moved the conversation along. "You know they have award-winning messenger pigeons on the roof. They still use them to send the morning grocery orders to Little Italy. Amazing, huh?"

The owner, cut through the crowd when he saw Nate and Maureen. He greeted them warmly and ushered us in ahead of everyone else. It reminded me of stories about Studio 54 and waiting to be one of privileged few to be allowed in. This time, it was I who was with Andy Warhol and one of the lucky, chosen few.

"Your guest is already here," he said leading us to our table.

The restaurant was brightly lit and loud in the way that an Italian family meal is on any given Sunday. The sound of utensils blended with laughter to create a joyous cacophony, while rich smells filled the air making me feel hungrier than I really was. The ambience was convivial though I wished it had been quieter and darker. Candles would have been a nice touch to help set the mood until Nate pointed his friend out.

After seeing him, the décor made no difference. Frank was even better than publicized. He was tall, with broad shoulders and was slightly tanned. As we got closer, I saw his hair was dirty blond and sun-streaked, and yes, he even had a five o'clock shadow. Guys like him wore the bronzed God look well, knowing it made their blue eyes even more spectacular. I didn't think fair guys could sprout a beard in a day, but he even had that going for him. He looked flawless in a sports jacket with suede elbow patches and jeans. K'ching, three cherries, he was just my type! Frank was artsy looking in a great, left bank poet kind of way.

Unceremoniously, Maureen said, "I'm going to hit the loo before I sit down. Join me," she demanded without asking if I wanted to. No sooner had we closed the bathroom door than Maureen shrieked, "Oh my God, he's even better than his picture. He's GORgeous!"

"Yes, ma'am," I replied. "Do you think he's the real deal?"

"Only one way to find out. We go back in there, then you charm the pants off him and maybe he'll reciprocate later," she laughed.

I walked towards the table, eager to get to know Frank. From a short distance, against his tan, his teeth looked even whiter than they might have been. It wouldn't have surprised me one bit if a star had twinkled from the corner of his smile, the way it did on the newly brushed teeth of Colgate commercials from years ago. He stood and pulled out my chair, holding out his hand to shake mine, but then changed his mind. He planted a quick kiss on my cheek instead and said, "So nice to meet you, Julia. I'm Francis but my friends call me Frank." It was awkward in lieu of combustible. I downplayed my disappointment, thinking the kiss had been subdued because we were in a crowded restaurant. I wondered if he could sense the letdown and felt an immediate flush rise. He was super handsome, so I rationalized that a friendly kiss shouldn't be the barometer for sensuality and the man deserved to be given a second chance. Thankfully the waiter approached the table just in time to divert everyone's attention from my crimson cheeks and my "Oh my God, he's hot as hell face."

Our waiter, Giovanni, recited the specials for what must have been a full five minutes and I hadn't heard a thing.

Maureen told him, "I'll have my usual."

"Signora," he asked looking in my direction.

"I'm sorry. I'm not quite ready. Would you come back to me?"

Nate said he would do the Shrimp Fra Diavolo and Frank was having the Chicken Saltimbocca.

Again, our waiter turned his attention to me. I was flustered. I hadn't been thinking of anything other than how handsome Frank was.

I said, "I'll have the penis." It wasn't until Maureen coughed up her Chianti that I realized what I had said.

"The penne I meant. His pasta looks great. I'll have that," I said pointing to the meal that a gentleman seated to my right was having. Thankfully it was the pasta that sounded like my faux pas.

"Perfetto. Penne ala Puttanesca," he said laughing. Nate laughed too.

When I asked Nate what was so funny, he simply replied that I couldn't have picked a more perfect dish. Happy to have made a good choice, I passed the bread basket, as Maureen poured the wine.

We started a casual conversation that carried on effortlessly, becoming increasingly more animated throughout dinner. Francis was smart, well-mannered, a world traveler, successful, handsome - and gay. It wasn't anything he said or did, but the inflection of his voice, coupled with the cadence of his speech that gave it away over time. Maureen and I both caught it, while Nate, happy in his ignorance, remained in the dark. Maureen bumped my leg with hers purposefully when it hit us around the same time. Sharing a secret made me feel like a schoolgirl. I could stop trying and just be myself. It felt liberating to be able to relax without feeling like I was on an interview. My life had been filled with them, both personally and professionally over the last few months. Taking a breather was a welcome change. Let's face it, undergoing a fact-finding session for a job was no fun, but doing it on a date was even worse. You had to be clever, witty, positive, and appear interested with just the right degree of sultriness built in. It was simply too much.

The conversation flowed freely, as did the wine. The meal had been delicious and I understood why my friends were still regulars despite the fact that the restaurant was no longer around the corner. Giovanni didn't even ask if we wanted desert. The owner had already packed some cannoli for his friends to take home. We hopped into the car after dinner and at my suggestion drove to Veniero's for dessert and cappuccinos. The Italian bakery on Manhattan's lower east side had originally been a distributor of sweets to the city's finest restaurants. Since then, it had become popular with foodie millennials and was now a trendy spot for coffee and pastries after an evening out. During the ride there, we all raved about our meals. I learned Maureen was also a great cook and had thought about opening a restaurant at one point. She had given up the idea but never the dream. When we arrived, the bakery was crowded, and the long line of mostly couples, was out the door. A table for four opened up after within minutes. We sat next to the hissing espresso machine, taking it all before ordering. The ornate copper ceilings glistened in the soft lighting and made it seem like everyone's eyes sparkled. It was a good look. Frank and I kidded each other, becoming very comfortable together. I could tell that Nate was excited and reading it all wrong. Maureen would surely set him straight once they were alone.

A few minutes after our desserts came, we started to wind down quickly. Maureen glanced at her watch. When she saw it was already after midnight, her demeanor changed instantly. She rose quickly. "Nate, we have to get home. I promised the sitter we would be back early. She has a swim meet tomorrow at 10:00 a.m. I swore we'd get her home in time to get a full night's rest. Besides I really need to get some sleep. The baby kicked my ass this week and I'm beat."

Completely out of character for him, he replied obediently, "Yes dear and before you say it, I'll also figure out what we owe Gabriela before we get home."

Frank waved him off as he tried to get the check. "Go on," he said. "I'll get this and take care of getting Julie home."

Nate winked at Maureen, then she winked at me. Nate thought he had played Cupid and his wife was obviously amused by his unplugged gaydar.

Frank and I lingered over the last few drops of cappuccino as the busboys cleaned the tables around us. When we finally stood, we realized that we were among the last few patrons in the café. Frank said, "I know it's late, but I'm wired from the coffee. Why don't I put you in a cab? I think I'd like to walk to my hotel."

"If you don't mind, I'll join you. It'll be good to have the time to wind down before bed and God knows I could certainly use the exercise after that dessert."

He nodded. As we walked out, I hooked my arm in his. He turned to me and said my name. Before he could finish his sentence, I said, "I know."

"Know what?" he asked.

"Relax. I know you are gay. Honestly Frank, it made the night so much better. I'm tired of putting on a dating face. It's really exhausting and so much damned work."

"I am so glad. I was hoping you weren't going to be disappointed," he replied obviously relieved. "I know exactly how you feel about dating. I've met so many Cretans recently that I'm starting to feel that 'alone' isn't a bad thing."

"Hey, take a number. That's my line," I answered giggling. We had a chuckle and enjoyed not having to pretend anymore.

Walking uptown, arms linked with a warm appreciation for one another, at least for tonight, we could let our guard down. We talked about how the search to find a partner in a big city seemed pointless at times. As we spoke, we came to the conclusion that it was not the urban landscape that made it difficult. It was a cultural change in the way people interacted that created the barrier. They insisted on broadcasting every aspect of their lives in cyberspace as though the rest of the world really cared. Our society had grown more self-centered. Frank told me that many of his dates were willing to share everything about their lives except themselves and it made having a relationship difficult. People were so busy with their toys and the trappings of success that it left little time for intimacy and conversation. I confessed that until recently my innermost thoughts were never shared with anyone except Lisa. It was a difficult pattern to break, but I was working on it as a worthy endeavor. We spoke about how people withheld their innermost feelings from others, yet online, they were eager to share them openly. Like a call for attention, it was as though they were begging to be noticed by the world at large while ignoring those closest to them. Frank found it embarrassing when people publicized their sexuality as though daring you to say something and had chosen to remain reserved about his preferences. I wondered if he'd ever come out to friends and family, so I asked him. We talked about it as we walked uptown, and though we addressed other subjects candidly, he never really answered my question.

We got to his hotel and he walked past it to accompany me home, saying he wanted to make certain I got there safely. I loved his manners and welcomed the old-school courtesy. It had been a great night. By the time we arrived at my place, it was past one in the morning. I invited him up for a nightcap anyway. We had such a fun evening that without hesitation, he accepted my offer and walked upstairs where Molly greeted us warmly. She was at ease with Frank from the start. I suggested he make himself at home while I took her out. Instead, he grabbed her leash, saying he loved dogs, and asked if he could walk her. She already knew the drill and was eager to go out. It would be fine since Frank seemed perfectly comfortable with her and Molly had taken an instant liking to him, so I chose to stay behind.

They came back about a half hour later. Both had gotten a jolt of energy from the walk and seemed ready for more socializing. We sat on the couch laughing almost nonstop at the idiosyncrasies of being single and of life in general. I learned that Frank had been married and was a bit skeptical about finding love again. Numerous strained relationships had burrowed their way under his skin. After just one evening, it felt as though we'd been friends for years. Without thinking how weird it would sound, I suggested, "If you want, spend the night. It's late and I've got a pullout."

"But we just met. Are you sure?" he asked.

"Positive. I won't even try to fulfill every woman's fantasy by seducing you. We'll just give the neighbors something to talk about."

"What's that all about anyway?"

"Every woman wants to feel that she is seductive enough to convert either a gay man or a priest. In my case, it has always been both!"

I reminded him to call the hotel so they would hold his room for the next day, opened the pullout, then gave him fresh towels and sheets. He kissed me on the cheek again and before turning in said, "I had a really good time tonight."

I woke up the following morning well rested and surprised that it was past nine and Molly hadn't woken me for her walk. The delicious smell of bacon had roused me. I knew there was none in the fridge and much less in the pan. I wondered if the windows had been open and I was smelling a neighbor's breakfast. I put on some sweats to investigate where the smell was coming from when Molly greeted me at the threshold of my bedroom with a telltale piece of crumbled bacon stuck to her chin. Frank smiled when he saw me and said, "We've already been on our walk, to Zabar's for a few supplies, and Molly walked me to the bagel place."

"You're too much, you know that? Do they make straight guys like you?"

He smiled, "I don't know, but if there are, I'm sure you'll find out. You're terrific Julie. Any guy would be a jerk not to pick up on that quickly."

We had just started having breakfast when the phone rang. It was too early for anyone else to be calling, so I figured it would be Nate looking for a post mortem.

"Hey, Jules. Sooooo?"

"So, Frank is great. You want to speak to him?"

"I knew it! You're not kidding me, right?"

"No, sir. He's right here making breakfast for Molly and me."

He called out to his wife triumphantly, "Maureen, Julie had an all-night play date. I knew you guys were perfect for each other. Go get'em girl."

I didn't have the heart to clue Nate in. I'm sure Maureen had tried to tell him, but he probably didn't believe her and now it would be too difficult to explain. At some point in our lives, each of us has misread a situation, calling it what we wanted it to be, rather than what it was. That was Nate's time.

"Why didn't you tell him?"

"Tell him what?"

"That you've got the wrong equipment for my team."

"First of all, because he didn't ask. Second of all, because he thinks I bagged a live one. He sounded really happy, so I didn't want to wreck it for him. And finally, because it is none of his damned business."

We had breakfast and read the Sunday times like the idealized New York couple would do over brunch. When it came time to part, we exchanged numbers and promised to stay in touch although both of us knew we wouldn't. We also knew that it would not be for lack of wanting the friendship, but between the distance and the lifestyle differences, cultivating one would be difficult. Common ground and proximity were crucial building blocks in friendships as much as in romance. Frank kissed me goodbye, roughed up Molly's "do", and stepped out of my life.

I got a call shortly after Frank had left. Ruth had already returned from her trip and wanted to catch up over coffee. She didn't bring up the reason for her impromptu trip and I didn't ask about it, thinking she would have shared had she wanted to. I filled her in on my week and my work at the shelter. Ruth was pleased I found a paying job and said, "Now you can look for the perfect job without being desperate to accept the first one that comes along." She added laughing, "You should consider doing the same thing with men."

She had become a friend as well as was one of my female mentors. Lisa had always been a great sounding board and now I had Ruth and Sheila as her back up. All three were opinionated, but quite different from one another. Sheila was assertive and forthright, while Ruth could be described as intelligent and convincing. And Lisa, well, Lisa was just the same as she'd always been, consistent and sensible. They had been a great influence on me. Each one had encouraged me in her own way to take technology classes and the training was paying off. Advanced Excel and Publisher were challenging at first, but as I became more adept, the courses became more interesting and ultimately easier. Once comfortable with the programs, I started to embrace my newly learned skills.

To a certain extent, we are all creatures of habit and most comfortable within the confines of what feels familiar. Sheila said the trick was to keep pushing the boundaries of one's comfort zone out a little more, each time broadening our sphere of knowledge and influence. I had come to trust her judgment and by testing her methodology, concluded that more often than not, she was right.

Lately, Lisa had added being a single's scout to her bag of tricks. She was always on the lookout for new venues that I could explore to meet men. Her boss' daughter met her husband through an organization called Meet in New York. As my social coordinator, Lisa felt a need to tell me about it and urged me to look it up online. It was advertised as a group for meeting like-minded people by participating in a group outings around the city. Past events seemed like fun and I thought it might be a good venue to meet men whose company would be enjoyable. The activities they hosted were focused mostly around cultural events, and right or wrong, I imagined most of the attendees would have a few more brain cells than the men I'd been dating lately.

On Sunday, the group had scheduled a scavenger hunt at the Metropolitan Museum of Art. I didn't have plans and called Ruth to see if she wanted to meet me there. Instead of coming, she replied, "Go and have fun. It's great that you are keeping busy. Just don't expect every activity to lead to your soul mate. When it is meant to be, it will be. Things will happen organically, in their own time, and not a moment before. So stop pushing." She was right, though her tone seemed somewhat jaded. I tried to convince her that my love of the arts was the driving factor, but we both knew better. I heard an edge in her voice and wondered if everything was okay. When I asked her, Ruth told me that she was just jet-lagged and that at her age, she didn't adjust well to moving between time zones.

I dressed in my favorite leggings and leather riding boots in the hopes of hunting instead of scavenging. Before leaving, I did my makeup immaculately, gave myself a great messy blow out, and was off to another adventure.

I made my trek to Museum Mile and pretended to love art much more than I did to embark on my search again. Arriving at the Met, I looked for the activities guide. Proud that I wouldn't be sitting on a barstool waiting for "the one" to come along, I found my group. Parents were kissing their kids goodbye and I wondered what the children would be doing while their parents were flirting with each other. Revisiting the activities listing on my phone, I saw what I had previously missed. The activity for which I had meant to register was the museum tour for singles and newly divorced parents. The scavenger hunt had been organized to keep the kids busy while their parents combed the Sculpture Garden getting to know one another. My group was comprised of kids in a broad range of ages. I tried to switch activities and was told the singles event was oversold. Suggesting this might be fun as well, the guide paired teams of two and partnered me with the tallest girl so I wouldn't feel so out of place among the pack of culture vulture 13-year-olds.

"Do you work here lady?" the Upper East Side brat asked me.

"No, I don't, "I'm here to have fun just like you."

She rolled her eyes at me. Thinking to myself that two could certainly play that game, I rolled my eyes right back at her. She fist bumped me looking impressed and instantly, I was accepted into her circle with no further questions asked. Making the best of it, we chatted. Marla was indeed an upper east side born and bred New Yorker, with a great sense of humor and a burgeoning love of art once you cut through her crap.

Ok, so today was not "soul mate day" but I decided to go with it and some have fun. When I realized that the Met Scavenger Hunt was just an extended version of the super-hot Pokémon Go game, I knew we would win. Marla and I hit every mark easily until we had to find milk near the steps leading from The Great Hall to the mezzanine. We had no idea where the hell to find milk inside the Met without buying it and then it came to me. I saw a young, trendy mom pushing a stroller to the coat check with another kid in tow. I told Marla to follow my lead and instructed her to chat the mom up about how cute her kids were, especially the three-year-old boy who was walking alongside the carriage. When she was fully engaged with the mom, I swiped the baby's bottle from the back pocket of the stroller, swiftly and deftly, as though born to crime. I motioned to Marla, by making a slicing gesture across my neck that it was time to cut the conversation short and run for the hills. She did, and we quickly walked up the steps and into the crowd, winded but elated.

"Man, oh man," she exclaimed. "That was unbelievably exhilarating."

"How old are you anyway?" I asked when the five-syllable word rolled off her tongue like she was born inside a library.

"I'm twelve," she replied, not fazed by the friendship she had now cemented with someone who was almost four times her age.

"Well then, what are you doing palling around with someone old enough to be your mother?"

"God, my mother would absolutely go crazy if she heard you say that! You are WAY older than my mom," she stated.

So, bruised ego and Metamucil in hand, we went to claim our prizes. When we ascended the steps in front of the Temple of Dendur, we were each handed two movie theater tickets and a glow stick. I had to laugh when we said our goodbyes and let Marla know how much fun it had been for me. She hugged me tight before we parted and asked if I wanted to go to the movies with her sometime. Flattered, I accepted the invitation, and we planned to make a Sunday matinee with her nanny in tow.

As I walked home briskly, I realized that what had started as a complete washout ended up being a really fun time. I'd even made a new friend. There was no harm in that. Perhaps Ruth was right. The best things in life were those that can't be planned for. You simply had to relax and let life have its way with you.

Under the guise of discovering whether or not Woody Allen still played there, my date with Paul was that Thursday. With another interview the day before my date, I was trying to temper my expectations with regards to both events. When the interview turned out to be a bust, I hoped it was not the precursor to a bad date ahead. To cheer myself up, I walked Molly to the park where I had promised her we would have a catch. I told her about how the interviewer had asked me a question, with so many acronyms in it that I froze. It was embarrassing and someone with my experience should have been able to handle it easily. By way of response, Molly licked my hand, weaseling the ball out of it as her way of telling me to get over it. I felt better after a game of catch and was grateful that she was in my life. Even then, shortly after becoming family, Molly had a way of minimizing my shortcomings by accepting me just as I was and loving me in spite of them. We had a delightful afternoon and I got home in plenty of time to get ready for my date.

On my way to meet Paul, I walked to the bus stop and the M5 arrived instantly. It was as though it had been waiting for me to show up. Broadway was bustling with people, but traffic was still moving nicely until we got to Central Park South. At the Plaza, hotel workers were protesting their wages, and like with everything else in New York, a crowd gathered to see what was going on. It brought traffic to a standstill. I got off the bus and walked, still hoping to arrive on time. When I got to Michael's Pub it was 7:10. I remembered what he

245

had said about being on time and shrugged it off thinking a few minutes would not matter. With city traffic being so variable, I was certain he would understand. At the threshold of the pub, I reached for the door and was surprised when it opened as if by magic. An attractive, well-dressed man on the other side of the door was stepping out. He stopped and said my name as I looked at him questioningly. "I'm Paul," he added.

"Paul, I'm so sorry to be late. I hit a lot of traffic and,"

"And nothing Julia. You just didn't plan well enough. I was just leaving," he said waiting for me to object.

I said "okay" and he said "okay" and then he stepped back into the pub. He seemed to be disarmed by my acceptance of his premature exit and had lost control of the exchange. Obviously, this was unknown territory for him and he was rendered speechless. Team "Don't Roll Over" just scored a point and the fans cheered.

We walked to a bar-side table in silence. When we sat, he apologized, "I'm sorry Julia, but punctuality is a thing with me. Please keep that in mind should there be a second date," he dictated.

Thank God for music. I hoped it was loud enough to drown out my lesson in manners. By the end of the set, we had settled into a more comfortable groove. I admit the cocktails might have helped. There's nothing like a little vodka to loosen up the "I could give two shits muscle". Between songs, we made small talk and started getting to know each other. After speaking with him for a while, he was actually quite nice and not nearly as overbearing as he initially appeared to be. I don't think I could have stayed if he had been.

"I'm an equities trader and quite well known in the industry. I have achieved a kind of celebrity status in my professional life and have a waiting list of future clients. Remind me, what is it that you do?"

"Me?" I asked, stalling for some time to conjure up a story. "Marketing for non-profit organizations."

"Impressive," he replied. "How many do you oversee?"

"About a dozen," I said, not sharing more than was needed. He didn't need to know I was talking about dogs. I had never been a good liar and it felt as though my face was on fire. Whether it was the cocktail or the half-truth that caused my cheeks to redden, I would never know, but if I wasn't sure about it, then hopefully, neither was he.

"Wow. That's huge. You must be really talented," he replied. As the evening progressed, I was glad to have given him the time to simmer. His flavor had definitely improved. Still, there was a hint of a domineering streak in his personality that reared its ugly head several times that evening. Despite it, for some reason, I was intrigued by him. He definitely liked to get his way, but having been in a management position where I made all the decisions for many years, it was a liberating change to be to hand the reins over to someone else. We were getting more comfortable together when he asked if I wanted to stay another set.

"I'd love to, but not on a school night," I replied.

"Okay, I'll walk you home then."

"No, thank you though. I really need to get home quickly. I've got an early start and need to get back to walk the pooch," I said.

"Oh, you have a dog?" he asked without inflection.

"Yes, Molly, a lovely, steel blue Great Dane," I replied.

"And a Great Dane no less," he added sardonically.

"Is that a problem?" I asked.

"Not yet," he replied. "It doesn't matter. The thing is, I have terrible allergies. I'll just have to take a decongestant in the mornings," he added putting the cart way before the dog. "Well then, I don't want to keep you."

"Good night," I said turning away and wondering if I should have said good riddance instead. I took the subway home and while opening the door, heard the phone ringing. I made it inside in time to pick up the call. It was Paul and I was surprised to hear his voice.

"You left in such a hurry, we didn't even get a chance to say a proper goodnight. I had a really nice time. How about seeing me again this weekend?"

"Sure. I'd like that." I was surprised and unsure of whether or not the statement was true.

We spoke for a while and the conversation flowed nicely. He seemed a little looser on the phone than in person. It was possible that it took him a while to warm up to people. That alone shouldn't have held me back, after all, I was the same way.

As we wrapped up the conversation he said, "Great. Well then, I'll see you Saturday. The weather is supposed to be perfect all week. We'll go for a ride in the country and a hike."

He didn't ask if I'd ever hiked or would enjoy it, but he seemed to be more interested than I was and that was a welcome change. I'd only tried hiking a couple of times in my life, and honestly those were more like walks in the woods. I was flattered by his attention but couldn't help wondering what his motivation had been. Was I that intoxicating or was it the fact that in his mind, I'd be easy to manipulate? I was starting to sound like Ruth.

I didn't want Molly to think I was an easy mark, so I turned my back to her while talking, but she would not be dismissed. I disregarded her and continued with my conversation even though she circled around me several times while cocking her head inquisitively. Molly put her paw on my leg when the call was coming to an end. Just as I was hanging up, she timidly squatted and peed right on the kitchen floor. She had never done that before and it surprised me. People said when a dog had an accident you were supposed to smack the its ass with a rolled-up paper and then hold its head close to the puddle and scream "NO." So, that's what I did.

When I yelled at her, she cowered and peed again. She looked frightened and I was immediately sorry for my actions. It had taken time to gain her trust, and now, with one mistake, I might have blown it. I recognized the horrible feeling of humiliation on her face and felt awful about it. I should have thought of her before taking the call, after all, it was over an hour later than her usual walk. It was unfair to reprimand her for something she couldn't control.

I laid some newspaper over the puddle and was grateful that it sopped up the mess quickly. Before leaving, I grabbed a trash bag and her leash to go for a walk, even though it was a bit too late. We made our way down to the garbage cans carrying the only sign of her mistake and as soon as we dumped it, her demeanor changed. Molly shook it off and became herself again. We enjoyed the walk and she seemed to have forgotten all about the incident.

When we went back inside, Molly became visibly anxious and made me feel even worse than before. Clearly, we both were somewhat insecure about whether or not a single mistake could throw things off kilter in a relationship. I looked at her, realizing that in many ways, our pasts shape us. She remained steadfast and tried to hold her head high, but she couldn't make eye contact and began to cower. It seemed as though we were both unsure of what action to take next and hoped we could both put our mistakes aside without letting them define us. I discarded what I had been told and replaced it with what I knew was right – forgive and forget. After all, what's a little pee among friends? I held her close and cuddled her so she would know that everything was okay. I whispered that she would always be safe with me and told her about a little adventure we would have. She loved making the trek downstairs to do laundry and a quick wash was in order since I had weekend plans. So off we went, thinking it would be a clever way to put the past behind us.

CHAPTER 11

REVELATIONS

I went down to the basement laundry room with Molly in tow later than I usually did. She loved to watch the clothes go around in the dryer as though expecting a hand with a ball to pop out. Laundry night usually meant a short walk to get a mini cannoli as a treat for each of us. She had grown to love the creamy filling almost as much as I did, but at half past nine, it was too late for one tonight. Besides, we had to watch our girlish figures. While separating the whites from the colors, a notice on the bulletin board caught my attention. It was a Groupon deal of the week for a virtual golf class at Chelsea Piers. The subtitle which read "A Great Way to Meet Singles" was what attracted me. It was a brilliant idea! Guys were always looking to improve their game and some dreamboat would be there, blissfully unaware that I would be moving in for the kill.

In my mind, golf was an old man's game more than a sport, and a pompous one at that. I hated the exclusionary feel of the country club and the loud, garish clothing for men. Even the non-descript attire for women was not something I could relate to, but without a date scheduled for Friday night, maybe a lesson would be a good way to spend the evening. I purchased the Groupon from my phone and left a message for Nate asking for a lift there on Friday. Winking at Molly as though it were our little secret, she responded with a sigh, then laid near my feet, under the folding table, never questioning when she'd meet that special someone. She already had – and it was me.

I dropped the whites into the machine when a loud noise echoed from the stairwell. Someone must have been dragging a huge bag of laundry down the steps. It sounded heavy, but I didn't think twice about it. Unlike me, Molly's ears perked up. She rose quickly, taking a step towards the thud and barking loudly several times. She rarely barked, but when she did, her voice alone made her size be known. I stepped closer to her. Her bark sounded convincingly vicious and reverberated into a low rumbling growl that sounded like it came from her gut. She ran towards the staircase. I followed her as someone threw the exit door open, setting off the alarm. Her coat was bristled down her spine and her lips were drawn back in a ferocious grimace which made her already large canines look bigger still. Molly was poised to fight. It surprised me to see how menacing she looked. I had never seen that side of her and remembered that her idiot owner had given her up for not being a guard dog. His loss was my gain. At that moment, she looked like Cerberus, the beast from hell. I followed my demonic leader out of the room to see what had happened.

A young woman lay on the floor in the stairwell, curled up in a fetal position, crying softly. She was shaking uncontrollably when I walked over. Seeing there was no longer any danger, Molly reverted to her calm and gentle nature, licking the woman's face gently until she started to regain some semblance of composure. I asked if she was okay. She didn't speak but kept whimpering softly while I called the police. We waited in silence with her until the police arrived a few minutes later. They came into the room with guns drawn, then slowly lowered them when they saw Molly laying protectively next to the woman. It was evident what scared the perpetrator off. The taller officer asked me a few questions while the other one took the girl's information. I told him I had seen her several times in the building but didn't know if she lived there or was a visitor. After he took my information, he turned his attention to the victim asking her name. It was Abigail. She was divorcing her assailment and he had already threatened her several times. He scared her, telling her what would happen if she didn't return, before accosting her in the stairwell. Trembling, she recounted the story. He had come up from behind her and held a knife to her throat, whispering that if she made a sound, he would slit it. Then, dragged her down the stairs saying the choice was no longer hers. The police listened attentively and told her not to worry. They would ensure her safety. After giving them the details of her assault, Abigail stood up slowly. She crouched down to hug Molly, thanking her. Abigail's tears fell on her heavily and made her coat glisten like mercury. Molly looked regal while standing perfectly still until the cops took Abigail to the precinct, where they would complete the report. She had risen to the occasion bravely, instinctively protective despite her fear, and stayed vigilant until we were the only ones that remained.

When we went upstairs, I dropped the laundry bag on the floor, relieved to be safe and back in my own apartment. I didn't want to think about what would have happened had we not been there. Although Abigail appeared to be in her thirties, she looked like a scared child, helpless after her ordeal. She had been lucky tonight, but I wondered what the future held for her.

I went into the living room, hoping that a late-night sitcom would help settle my nerves. Molly followed me in. Though not allowed on the furniture, she was big enough to pop a hip up on it, like a lady sitting in a parlor when I wasn't looking. She was extremely resourceful and had found a work-around to the "no dogs on the furniture" rule. It made me laugh, and often, I would pretend not to see her doing it. That evening, I made an exception, inviting her up to join me. We sat together for a long time trying to make sense of all that had happened. After hearing me out, Molly got off the couch. I followed her into the bedroom where it became evident that some rules were optional. She had already curled herself up into a semicircle at the foot of my bed and I didn't have the heart to tell her to get off. She had earned it. Falling asleep almost instantly, her snoring had become my white noise. It was a peaceful sound that I found comforting each night as it lulled me to sleep.

In the morning, I focused on the week ahead over a leisurely cup of coffee. After reading every article of interest in the newspaper, at Sheila's behest, I practiced interviewing for the rest of the day. By evening, the process felt natural and my responses were more authentic. The hard work would hopefully pay off during my interview the next day. I was fiddling around with the layout for a newsletter when my phone rang. I wouldn't have answered it, had it not been Nate I heard recording a message. "Hey, Toots. What time do I have to swing by for you Friday night?"

I picked up the receiver and said, "What do you mean?"

"Is that you? I thought I was talking to a machine. Did you forget, Ms. Didrikson? You asked me to drive you to your golf lesson."

"Thanks for reminding me. A lot has happened since then. It must have slipped my mind after practice interviewing all day. I'm sorry, I should have called you to cancel. I'm not going."

"What do you mean you are not going? No choice Babe. You said you already paid for the class and it couldn't have been cheap. These days, money doesn't grow on trees for you. Go. What have you got to lose?"

"I don't know."

"Go. I need the fare," he joked.

"I guess you've got a point, but… oh, what the hell. The lesson starts at 6:30 p.m. so I guess 6:00 will do." Becoming more excited about it I added, "I'll be the belle of the golf ball and make a grand entrance. I bet the class will be filled with men waiting for me to give their lives meaning."

"I thought you were already doing that. Make it 5:45 instead Cinderella. West Side traffic can be at a standstill on a Friday night."

For the interview, I selected a more casual outfit, and felt more composed, dressing differently than I would have a month ago. Without knowing whether to attribute the change to experience interviewing with several under my belt now, to the wardrobe change, or to the practice runs, I presented a more confident me to my potential employer. Whatever the formula was, it worked. I spoke candidly, with assurance about my skills and experience. Regardless of what the catalyst had been, I aced the interview and was offered a freelance marketing project on the spot. It paid well, so I accepted the offer immediately, knowing it would help supplement my work at the shelter to pay the bills.

The freelance job was for another non-profit organization. The flexibility both jobs provided left me time to look for a more lucrative, full time opportunity, but I wasn't sure whether I would or not. I enjoyed having the time to structure the workload as I saw fit and found the work rewarding. My weeks were full and I liked not having to rush through each task, taking time to enjoy the process. I even made time for an extra coffee with Ruth before I readied myself for the first golf lesson. Jumping into the shower and scrubbing like I was going to learn golf in a Petri dish, I emerged raw, but slightly shiny, and thought it was a good look. I slipped into a pair of Chinos, carefully ironed and creased. Before leaving, I put on some perfume and a polo shirt along with sensible shoes. I gave myself a thorough once over in the mirror when a text from Nate popped up. It read: *Madame, your carriage awaits.* I kissed Molly goodbye and locked the door on my way out.

"I see you've finally transitioned into comfortable shoes," he said turning to greet me. As his eyes moved up to my face, he added, "My, don't we look waspy tonight."

"I'm the poster girl for a Connecticuter without a husband," I shot back. "Doesn't this outfit just scream GOLF to you?"

"If you say so, but I'm not so sure what you are wearing is a good look for attracting men. It might be better suited if you are done with guys and ready to switch teams," he said, quickly adding,

"But that's not a problem, I'd love you anyway. Live and let live, right Julianna?"

"Yes sir. You know, it's a good thing I'm getting to know you, otherwise, I wouldn't have been able to sense a compliment buried in there somewhere."

We caught up and chatted while he drove. Nate loved being a dad. He said that Mery was growing quickly and looked different from one week to the next. Maureen was back at work but it was tough for her. Although she loved her job, she missed the baby terribly and was torn between being a mom and an executive. She was learning quickly about the sacrifices that had to be made to have both and was leaning towards consulting from home instead. After he filled me in, I told him about what had happened in the laundry room and about how Molly had known instinctively that something was wrong.

"They say that dogs can sense fear and danger because they smell it. Boy, that woman was lucky that Molly is a spoiled laundress at heart."

"No kidding. I was so proud of her. It's funny, you know, I can't believe how much she has come to mean to me in a matter of months."

"When Mery is older, we'll get a dog from your shelter. Pets are a great way to teach kids how to nurture and take responsibility."

The traffic on the West Side Highway was surprisingly light. The ride was quicker still when we made every light. Before I left, Nate said goodbye as usual, wishing me "Happy Hunting".

I walked into the makeshift driving range feeling as though I was really strolling into a country club in the moneyed greens of Westport. There were quite a few women milling around with cocktails in hand. Unlike Westport, the cocktails were in plastic cups rather than fine crystal. I guess if you were slumming by playing make believe golf, sacrifices had to be made. The women were impeccably groomed. Dressed for the kill, they looked like they were going to an upscale cocktail party, and I, like the caddy for a group of stodgy businessmen. Maybe Nate had been right about my wardrobe choice. I hadn't dressed provocatively enough. The other ladies in the room showed a little leg and a lot of cleavage. There was not a man in sight. The men had to be in the adjacent bar having a drink prior to the lesson. Peeking in through the doorway, I saw a single lonely man sitting at the bar, looking like a beaten dog. I wondered where the rest of the students were. Looking around casually, I saw a couple of women who looked familiar, but couldn't place how I knew them. One lady waved me over. Welcoming the invitation, I joined her and said, "Hi, I'm-"

"Hi Julia. I remember you from speed dating."

"Ah," I replied having a flashback to that evening. "It's nice to see you here. Is this your first virtual golf class?"

"Sure is. I'm super excited. Golf is a fantastic way to meet men."

"Yep," I answered trying not to look too desperate. "I've been meaning to learn how to play for quite a while. I don't really consider golf a sport, but I'm told it is a great hobby for when you retire," I said quietly muttering to myself before adding, "Which I'm getting closer to every day and not by choice."

My thoughts drifted away for a moment to the future. People said that golf was something you could play into your eighties for exercise. Since the clock never stopped ticking, I envisioned myself as just another batty octogenarian hitting golf balls into passing cars on the West Side Highway. It wasn't a good visual. The woman's voice forced me back to the present.

"Don't kid a kidder girlfriend. Look around you. We are all here for the same reason and of course, all the men are late to the party."

"It's early yet. Class isn't supposed to start for another 15 minutes."

"I hope they show. I'm planning to meet an executive in the financial community and counting on pillow talk to help build my nest egg!"

We chatted awhile longer. When the guy at the bar walked in, he clapped his hands and said, "Ladies, ladies, simmer down. Each of you grab a club, and let's get going."

"But where are all the men?" a lady from the back asked.

"You are here to learn how to play golf, not to troll for men," he said sounding like the mother superior in a Catholic school. When I laughed out loud, he must have thought there was a serious student among us, because he began searching the room looking for his star pupil. Remembering what I was wearing, I feared being singled out immediately since my outfit could have passed for a parochial school uniform. My only departure from the regimented look was the lacy bra that no one could see and the fact that I smelled great. Perfume always had a way of making me feel feminine, no matter what I was wearing, so I never left home without it.

Not being able to find his protégé, our pro introduced himself as Adam, and started the class by showing us the correct way to hold a club. He looked like he was pissed off before we even began. His only caveat was, "Don't choke it like you do everything else." Fed up with women, and with this group in particular, after scolding us, he gave a preliminary primer on the art of putting. Standing us all in a line, left shoulder to the screen, except for the 2 lefties who stood in the opposite direction, we began.

"One and two and three and putt," he yelled as though directing an all-girl school production of *A Chorus Line*.

After 15 minutes of putting on a small Astroturf green, he moved on to driving. Adam motioned towards the clubs labeled "drivers" and instructed each of us to select one. This rudimentary part of the lesson took place on virtual golf course projected on to a huge screen. The image changed to a panoramic view of the greens with a flag marking a hole in the distance. First, he showed us how to drive the ball. It looked easy enough until he recruited a volunteer to demonstrate. It took a while for her to catch on. When he was comfortable that she had it, he stepped aside and instructed her to mimic his smooth motions solo, before the group tried it. Of course, he had selected the prettiest woman in the bunch who coincidentally also had the deepest cleavage and no hand/eye coordination. Left to her own devices, it was evident she was a hazard. Though Adam moved to the side, he was too busy staring at her to realize he was still in the line of fire. She positioned herself and when ready to swing the club, smiled at Adam. He nodded for her to proceed and that she did, clocking him right in the nuts with a masterfully driven golf ball. He fell to his knees and might have passed out had it not been for my laughter. Hearing it, his anguish was replaced with anger. When the sharp pain subsided, he started to regain his strength. Rising slowly to his feet, Adam asked, "Well, now that one of you has finally castrated me, can we continue?"

The incident was the highlight of the lesson. I had gone hunting again and though still alone when I walked out, it had been fun. At the end of class, the instructor dismissed each of us by handing out his card and saying, "I'm available for private lessons if any of you are interested."

I walked up to him to ask a question, and he quickly assumed I would inquire about the cost of private instruction.

"Eighty an hour and a buck twenty for ninety minutes," he said.

"Thank you," I replied. "But that's not what I wanted to know. When you walked into the room, without looking up you said 'Ladies, Ladies'. How did you know we were all women in the class?"

"You always are. Ever since the New Yorker ran the article about the best places to meet men, I teach only middle-aged women. Guys used to come for instruction in large buddy groups and teaching them was fun. Now, if I were to come prepared, I'd be wearing a hockey mask and a protective cup. With you ladies learning, golf has become a contact sport. You hungry Upper

Eastsiders have scared all the men away. Thanks for nothing," he added dismissively.

Now I understood why he was so pissed off from the start and thanked him for his patience as the spokeswoman for the group. At least I'd learned how to hold a golf club, and gotten a sense of the game that knew I'd never play again in my misguided search for romance.

It was still early, so I started my journey home by walking the High Line. The leisurely stroll felt like an indulgence and I was surprised by how enjoyable it was.

The night had been filled with firsts for me, so once in the apartment, I continued breaking ground by treating myself to a lovely dinner. My meals usually consisted of slapping something together since it was only me. That evening, I treated myself like company. I sautéed several large shrimp along with broccoli rabe in garlic and oil. The aroma was heavenly. As the artisan pasta boiled, I enjoyed a glass of Cabernet while setting the table for myself as though I were company. Under the guise of fueling up for the following day's hiking trip, I savored seconds and found immense pleasure in being in the moment.

After dinner, I engaged in my "deep dive" beauty routine. The process had been much less complicated when I was younger, but with middle age, extended pampering was needed to accentuate the good and airbrush the other. While dying my roots, I thought about how beautifully both Molly and Ruth wore their gray and wondered if I would ever have the confidence to do the same.

Paul was scheduled to pick me up at 8:00 a.m. and when he showed up two minutes late, I teased him, saying that punctuality was a thing for me too. Of course, he wasn't amused and said that my watch had to be wrong. Pointing to his wrist, his Breitling showed eight on the button and I wondered if he'd changed it before arriving just to be right.

Molly, who was laying in the living room, came to the door to greet my visitor. Apparently fearful of her, Paul stepped back into the narrow hallway a bit too quickly. Had it not been for the banister, it might have ended badly.

"Molly, this is Paul, my friend," I said reaching out and touching his arm to let her know it was okay.

Paul said, "Gather your things. I'll wait in the car. I don't like dogs and besides, I'm allergic to them."

"Come on, let's have a cup of coffee. You said it was a long ride. Sit for a few minutes while I brew some."

"No Julia, not while that beast is staring at me. She's a monster and looks eager to maul me. I'll wait for you downstairs."

I looked at her and smiled, "Monster my ass. She's an angel." He was already too far away to hear my assessment.

I finished packing up our snack of homemade trail mix, brie and crackers, as well as a half bottle of wine. Before leaving, I patted Molly's head and assured her not to worry, telling her he was a fool and didn't know any better.

When I walked outside, I saw that Paul was driving my dream car and gasped, "Oh my God, the 550

SL is my favorite car ever. It's even in midnight blue with a British tan interior. It's perfect!"

"Would you like to drive it?" He asked without hesitation.

"I'd love to but I wouldn't feel comfortable."

"Nonsense," he said. "Nothing is going to happen and what if it does?" he asked casually.

I was impressed. For a guy who seemed super uptight, he was pretty laid back about the whole car thing, so I decided to take him up on it.

He tossed me the keys and from the minute I sat behind the wheel, I felt like a marionette. Swerve left, speed up, and hug the curb were his words of endearment. What could have been a leisurely drive up the Henry Hudson to 9W turned into the Grand Prix of Monaco with me as Grace Kelly on the hairpin turns. It had been the epitome of a white-knuckle ride.

He told me to drive faster, saying the car could handle it. Rather than telling him I was not comfortable, I did what he said. I hadn't driven in a while and found the high speed challenging on the winding road. When we hit 70 miles an hour, the sound of a siren broke through the silence with its insistent shrill wailing, as a police car's lights flashed in my rearview mirror. I started to slow down, but Paul convinced me that the patrol car wasn't signaling us and told me to keep going. Though hesitant to listen, I did so. It was his car after all. Then, the cop pulled up alongside me and honked his horn loudly, signaling me to pull over.

Without missing a beat, Paul said, "Sure, now the cop will be tougher on us. You should have moved to the shoulder when he first asked you to."

Was this guy a nut or the best revisionist historian ever?

"Slow down and pull over to your right, by the edge of the road. Do it quickly, you've got a car coming up about 150 feet behind you. You have to park before he passes," Paul fired his commands off like he was orchestrating a tactical maneuver.

We prepared to go through the usual routine. I saw the trooper walking towards us with his hat on and chin strap in place. His badge shone in the autumn sun. I handed the officer my license, while Paul gave him the insurance card and registration. He walked back to his car, and after he spent some time there, he came back with two tickets. One was for going over the speed limit and the other for driving with an expired license. He told us I could no longer drive and asked to see Paul's license. Paul showed it along with a business card, either to drum up business or to perpetuate his illusions of grandeur. Once the trooper left, I unbuckled my seat belt to switch seats with Paul, but before I could get out of the car, he accosted me.

"Why hadn't you told me your license was expired?"

"I didn't know," I said. "My birthday just passed and I hadn't realized that my license lapsed," I answered defensively.

"Hey, don't get defensive just because you have a problem with authority."

"No, that's not it. I just don't like getting a summons and am starting to resent your telling me what to do at every turn."

Diverting the conversation Paul said, "Forget about it. Let's go have some more fun."

"More fun? That was about as much fun as waterboarding."

"Just follow my directions on the hike, not like while you were driving, and we'll be fine. Stop being so combative."

I wouldn't exactly call what he was doing giving direction. It was more like a drill sergeant barking orders during the Bataan Death March, with me complying like an already broken prisoner of war. It took me a full minute to soften my balled fists after hearing his newest command. My palms were clammy and there were beads of perspiration on my forehead. Even though several minutes had passed, I was still upset and wondered whether my initial instincts about Paul had been right.

A few miles up the road, he pulled over to the curb and said, "Come on, let's get out. We can start the hike from here. We have challenging trail ahead and it will only get worse with more people on it later." I didn't understand why that would pose a problem, but didn't care enough to have him explain it. He turned off the car and popped the trunk. I sat a while longer, then got out as he was removing something for it. Stepping around to see what he was doing, I watched as he proceeded to take out a thick rope and a pair of leather work gloves. Fuck me. Had he pulled out a shovel, I'd have been sure I was going to get killed in the woods and become fodder for the six o'clock news.

"What are the rope and gloves for?" I asked with suspicion.

"What, these?" he responded mischievously smiling as he closed the trunk. "You'll see."

"What about the treats I packed?"

"Not where we're going. It's steep and besides, if you eat now, you'll lose your lunch when you see what I have in mind."

I had visions of myself on a mountaintop, hands tied behind my back, feet akimbo being shtupped under a canopy of trees. Hum, that could have had potential if I wasn't mortified.

"Hold on while I make a call." I dialed Lisa's number quickly and she answered. You could almost hear how amused she was.

"So, how's the date with Mr. Punctuality going?"

"Lis, his trunk is stocked like he is auditioning for the lead on the next season of Extreme Survivor and he's taking me up a mountain with rope," I whispered.

"Are you kidding? Want me to call the cops?" she asked whispering as though he might hear her.

"Not yet. I'm going willingly but I just want you to know where I am in case I don't come back."

"Are you crazy? Get the hell outta there."

"No, I'll be fine. He has a tiny mean streak, but he's really handsome in a straight-laced army man way. To be honest with you, the control thing gives me a little bit of a thrill. I'm on Route 9W, fittingly just past the military academy on the Hudson."

"That's not enough information. Tell me exactly where you are?"

"Hey, what's the name of the trail?" I called out to Paul.

"Breakneck Ridge," he shouted back

"Are you serious? Did I hear Breakneck Ridge? Julie, don't go," I heard her say right before the connection dropped.

We walked up the trail easily for about fifteen minutes before it became a much steeper climb. I guess we had hiked another half mile or so when the trail became more difficult still and wasn't as well-marked. They had surely named it properly. The terrain was rockier but still doable. I wished I had worn hiking boots because I could feel the rocks through my sneakers and it was uncomfortable. I went along with the program anyway, trying to be a good sport until we came to what looked like a rock facing to me. I looked left, then right, without seeing a way to continue, and assumed we had come to the end of the trail. I was relieved though heaven knows I would have never given in. Competitive, my ass – I was out to prove he wasn't the only one with conviction, but since we had reached the end, thankfully I wouldn't have to.

"Come on," he motioned as he climbed the rocks confidently. It didn't look like he was kidding.

What had taken him about a minute to climb, took me four times as long.

"I thought you said you go to the gym?" he asked.

"I do, but I don't scale the rock climbing wall," I replied angrily.

"Julie, this most definitely is not rock climbing. It is an exhilarating hike on a beautiful day with a lovely woman." He was a jerk, but boy, did he have a way with words. He sounded so sweet when he wasn't in bastard mode that I could follow him to the end of the earth. Then, it occurred to me, that maybe I was already doing just that.

When I made it up to where he was waiting, he asked, "Can you make it or do you want to head back?"

I considered going back, then looked down and it seemed that the descent would be worse than the climb had been.

"I'm fine," I lied.

"Good, we'll go on then. Come on."

He swiftly maneuvered around a steep passage of large boulders where one slip could have easily landed me in a climber's hell. The only difference was Dante wouldn't be there to greet me and neither would Francesca or Ugolino.

When I caught up, or rather, when I made it up to where he was waiting, I asked him, "How much longer is it?"

"Only about five more miles," he said. After a few seconds he added quietly, "The next four hundred feet are a lot stepper so you have to be really careful. After that, there is only one tricky passage, then it's all downhill."

400 feet and steeper, was he kidding? What did he think I was, a yak? His quiet warning of what was to come scared me more than a little. I forced a weak smile as a bead of sweat rendered me temporarily

blind. That was the last thing I needed to ensure a plunge to my death from a misstep.

He proceeded upward without asking if I needed help or waiting for me. I watched incredulously while gripping a tree trunk for dear life. Two young Japanese women, in hiking sandals, passed me like mountain goats. Unbelievable! Then a guy in Five Finger sneakers climbing like Spiderman paused alongside me. "You okay?" he asked.

"I'm fine," I nodded and he went on with his climb. After about a minute I called out, maybe too quietly, "I lied," but he was already too far away to hear me. I couldn't see Paul and was frightened to go either up or down.

After several seconds, I heard the sound of a conversation getting closer and thanked God I wasn't as alone as I felt. Two climbers came up alongside me, confidently scaling the rocky climb. Seeing me paralyzed with fear, they paused and spoke to each other. The boy called out to me, "Hey lady, give my dad your hand and he'll help you."

The stranger reached down and took my hand to help me up. "For the next part of the trail, follow me, nice and easy. Look for the natural handholds and footholds. They will make choosing the best path much simpler."

I let myself be led, proving I had no problem with authority if you didn't come off like the Marquis De Sade. As evidenced by my reaction to this saint in hiker's clothing, at times I could even be a good follower.

It took a few more minutes to reach Paul who was chatting up the sandal girls while they posed for selfies.

"Hey," he said smirking. "I thought I was going to have to find another date for the descent." He said it teasingly, looking somewhat annoyed. Clearly, it was his way of indicating that he wanted me to speed it up. I would have gladly complied had I been able to and was already too tired to even be pissed off.

"Asshole," I mumbled under my breath. I thought I heard an echo, but it was the guy who had helped me, now repeating the same sentiments.

I thought about calling to see if a friend could pick me up. Before trying to make the call, I realized there was no way of letting them know how to reach me.

"Don't be a bad sport," Paul chided. "Let's move on."

"I need to rest a moment and catch my breath."

We were on a landing and the view was spectacular. I could see the whole Hudson Valley across the river as well as West Point. It was gorgeous. Had he not been such a jerk about it, we could have had a wonderful day.

"This looks like a good spot, right?" my guardian angel asked his son. "What do you think?"

His son looked around, then nodded, as his father reached into the backpack. He took out a picnic lunch, along with a couple of water bottles, some wipes and a foldable mat to sit on.

They had picked a beautiful area to have lunch and had made it up there with a movable feast. All this and I wasn't even allowed to bring some snacks! I had picked the wrong team to follow yet again. I considered offering up one of Paul's kidneys for a bottle of water, as he continued to hike undeterred and was well ahead of me again.

"Come on or I'll have to call the Whambulance," Paul shouted down to me. Without thinking, as Pavlov well knew I would, I responded to the bell.

He threw down a rope and said, "Tie this around your waist and I'll help bring you up." I did as instructed and felt like a container being hoisted onto a big cargo ship. Shaking from head to toe, I realized that even if he was a dick, he was the only thing keeping me safe at the moment and for that, I was grateful.

The pitch of our ascent had increased as promised. At one point, it felt like a vertical climb to me. Even worse, there were pine needles on some of the rocks that made it more difficult to negotiate the terrain. I took it one step at a time and didn't care that Paul was sighing loud enough for me to hear. Fuck him if he wasn't happy with my rate of progress. I was doing the best I could. If that wasn't good enough, then it was just too bad.

Finally making it up to where he was, I asked, "Why didn't you ask if I was up to this? You shouldn't have assumed without giving me an idea of what it would be like. The height scares me to death. This trail is treacherous for someone inexperienced and you didn't even care."

"That's nonsense. Of course I care, but it will only get worse as it gets darker, so we really need to watch the time."

We finished the climb in silence. Paul seemed to take some misogynistic pleasure in having broken my spirit. His actions spoke louder than his words, and at that point, I wasn't impressed with either of them.

Maybe I was blowing it out of proportion but without another option at the moment, I decided to give Paul the benefit of my uncertainty and called out to him, asking that he wait up. He stayed by my side during the descent, but neither of us uttered a word. We took the switchback trail down to make it a little easier. Though not happy with me, at least he took my abilities into consideration for the second half of the journey.

When we got back to the car, he tossed me the keys. Incredulously I said, "You've got to be kidding me. I've had more than my share of fun for one day. Besides, I can't drive now, remember?"

"Suit yourself," he said.

We drove the 65 miles in silence. When he pulled up in front of my building, he started to park.

"What are you doing?"

"I'm parking and getting my overnight bag," he said authoritatively.

"Are you kidding me? Don't you see how pissed off I am? You could have gotten me killed."

"But I didn't," he replied. "I can understand if you were angry at first. Now that you have had time to cool off, you should just feel accomplished."

I looked at him incredulously and had to restrain myself from answering as I would have liked to. "Yeah right. Thanks for scaring the daylights out of me. Maybe I'll see it differently tomorrow, but at the moment, I don't envision that happening."

"Okay, have it your way, however, do it upstairs so we don't make a scene."

"You know what, you are too much. What makes you think you are coming upstairs? I'm going and you're staying."

"The lady has a temper. Next time, we'll stay at my place so we don't have to deal with the dog. When will I see you again?" he asked.

"I'm not sure you will. You should have been honest with me. Once you saw the hike was above my pay grade, you should have cut it short. Besides, 'the dog' is part of my life, not an inconvenience. Molly comes with the package," I replied.

His answer caught me off guard. Paul said he was sorry after stuttering a bit and tripping over the words he was so unfamiliar with. He hadn't known how uncomfortable I'd been or he would have reacted differently. After his apology, Paul promised to make it up to me with a romantic belated birthday dinner. He kissed me goodbye on the forehead promising to call during the week. His attitude indicated that I should have jumped at the invitation, but maybe that was just a guy thing. In their own minds, some men can turn a no into a maybe. Perhaps he was being true to his gender and not so bad. After all, I did get an apology.

I was relieved and thankful to be able to plop down on the couch. My muscles were already tightening up. It was inevitable that I'd be aching the next day.

As Paul had alluded to, I had already started to feel pretty good about my accomplishment. Had he not been such a prick about it, I might have given him credit for pushing me through the petrifying hike. I reminded myself to be sure to take a couple of Ibuprofen before bed to stave off any inflammation. Before doing so, I remembered my promise to call Lisa when I was home safely. Speed-dialing her number, the phone rang only once before she picked up.

"Thank God it's you. I was getting worried when I hadn't heard from you."

"Thanks. I'm fine." I replied wearily.

"How'd you ever get home without the creep?"

"What creep? Oh, you mean my new boyfriend?" I asked only half kiddingly. "Funny how things change, huh. He drove me back and we made amends at the end of a long, quiet ride. Would you believe he actually thought he was spending the night?"

"Asshole," Lisa sighed.

Molly uncharacteristically barked her agreement.

"He may be, but for now, it seems he's my asshole. He is taking me for a romantic dinner next week."

"Sometimes, I just don't get you. You make the same mistakes over and over again. Go ahead. Keep stubbing your toe until you have to scream uncle. I'm glad you are home. Goodnight," she mumbled with frustration, not waiting for a response before hanging up.

That was the third time, no wait, the fourth time Paul had been called an ass that day. I wondered what his record was.

Molly and I went for our evening walk. I dreaded thinking about how much my muscles would ache the next day, since I was already having trouble negotiating the stairs.

When we got back, I saw that Paul had called and listened to his message. He was going be away midweek on a last minute business trip and was eager to see me before the weekend. He wanted to know if I was available for my birthday dinner the following night. After debating it, I returned his call and we firmed up our date. He planned to pick me up at seven, to which I added sharp, just to be difficult. We spoke for a few more minutes before hanging up. I slept soundly that night. Exhaustion always had a way of ensuring that. Although Paul had taught me a lesson very much in the wrong way, I was proud of my accomplishment. I had never really pushed the boundaries of my physical comfort zone until that day and it felt good. The fatigue helped me relax and fall into a deep sleep. I awoke nine hours later with an optimistic outlook wrapped around lots of aches and pains.

I struggled out of bed hobbling like a Neanderthal and thought stretching might help me get through the day. I slowly made my way to Perfect Fitness for a class to work out some of the kinks. My memory had selectively airbrushed the previous day and I now thought of the whole hike as a challenging adventure instead of the harrowing experience it had been in real time. My muscles knew better. My quads were on fire. When Natalie, the cheerful instructor said, "Now let's target those thighs with some squats," I walked out without a moment's hesitation. On the way home, I stopped at Starbucks. When I handed him the money for my coffee, true to form, Isaac stared at my hands and said, "You are one hot mess."

"Thanks for the compliment." My hands were in bad need of a manicure, especially after the prior day's nature worship.

"Well aren't you Ms. Optimism today. I didn't mean it in a good way. You look like a wash woman!"

He put my cup into a paper bag indicating his desire that I take it to go. What a bastard! I had planned to do that, but his smug remark and actions made me rethink it. Although I had a bunch of errands to run, just to show him who was in control of the situation, I gingerly settled into an easy chair, slowly to savor my coffee. After about an hour or so, I went back to get Molly so we could spend the afternoon at the shelter.

Our marketing efforts had significantly helped tell our story and resulted in three adoptions that day. With additional volunteers now, my schedule was even more flexible. As long as I handled the early morning walk and fed the dogs, we tag-teamed during the busier times. It worked out well and gave me free time for other things. I wondered how I had ever managed to fit in life when I was working 65 hours a week. It became painfully clear that maybe I hadn't.

My thoughts drifted to the upcoming date with Paul and I went home to get ready. I made a concerted effort to look pretty and wore the dress that had always been my favorite for a special dinner. I put my hair up. Wearing the necklace Matthew had given me, probably Katie's lost pearls, I remembered the superstition that pearls brought tears. Even with more than my share of lousy dates in my dossier, I was still a romantic and hoped that they would be happy ones.

Paul arrived precisely on time and refused to come inside, saying that he didn't want to be late. I knew better. It was Cerberus, who was keeping him at bay. I chuckled, patting her on the head as had become second nature to me now before leaving.

We drove to the restaurant in his beautiful car. He warned the valet to treat her gently and then gave him a ten-dollar tip to ensure that the veiled threat be taken seriously. Once inside, the atmosphere was as exactly as he had described it. The place was very romantic, old school elegant, and just dark enough to hide imperfections without being too dark to read the menu. It was a study in decorating genius.

Paul asked if he could order for both of us. Since it was his favorite restaurant, he was very familiar with the menu and I thought it a good idea. At least, he had asked, so we were making progress. He reached for my hand while we enjoyed our cocktails. The white truffle ravioli appetizer was the best thing I had ever tasted. Paul laughed when I told him it would be my meal choice right before they fired up the electric chair. Each course was better than the one which preceded it. The chef spoiled us with special tastings throughout the dinner and deboned our fish at the table. After savoring our dessert with a quiet conversation, we stood to leave. Before sending us off into the cool night, they handed us a bag with biscotti for our morning coffee. I guess this meant we were officially a couple now.

The evening had been special and the warm feelings I felt for Paul surprised even me. He had exceeded my expectations and I was impressed with how interesting the conversation had been. Perhaps I'd judged him too quickly. In the past, I had gone full force into relationships without first getting to know the person and it wasn't fair to either myself or the guy. A couple of dates had afforded Paul the requisite time he needed to mellow and led me to develop a positive outlook on us. When we parted, I was truly looking forward to our next date and hoping he aged like fine wine. Pleased with myself for displaying patience, I begrudgingly rethought the adage about teaching old dogs new tricks.

I used the following week to test drive some of my newly learned computer skills by designing a brochure for the non-profit freelance gig. Proud of myself, I had to admit it looked pretty damn good. Before I accepted the project, I did not know much about the organization or the work they did, so I made it my business to learn about them in short order. When I told Lynne about it, she began rattling off all their recent accomplishments. Preemies were their big push now, so Lynne suggested I stop by the hospital to experience what went on in a neonatal intensive care unit thinking it would give me a better understanding of their efforts. We coordinated my visit to Mount Sinai for later that week.

It was exciting to learn new things. As I learned more, my curiosity peaked. I used Constant Contact to build a database for direct mail and after sending out postcards, Family Friends saw a 12% increase in donations. When Sheila heard about it, she was very supportive and suggested that perhaps, it was my new calling. She was just being kind and I didn't really give it serious consideration until she added that success was like rabbits. I cocked my head to signal my confusion, as Molly would have done had she been there. When she saw my puzzled expression, Sheila explained that a few successes breed many more. Lynne was pleased with our progress as well and had credited the increase both in funds and in traffic largely to my efforts. It was rewarding to work with organizations that helped others. It forced me to focus on something other than myself. For the first time in forever, I felt proud of my work and wanted to make the feeling last.

On Thursday, as planned, I walked up to Mount Sinai and met Lynne in the lobby of the Klingenstein Pavilion. I hated hospitals and did everything in my power to avoid them. The smell alone brought back memories of losing my mother and sickened me. Having to fight the urge to leave, while I waited for Lynne, I looked around the lobby. The staff was friendly and looked happy to be of assistance. After several minutes of people watching, Lynne walked out of the elevator with a man and a dog. I didn't think dogs were allowed in hospitals and seeing it surprised me. As though reading my mind, Lynne smiled and told me the terrier was there to work. When I looked at the dog more closely, I noticed he was wearing a vest that indicated he was a volunteer. Lynne went on to say that Molly would make a great one. She was big enough that she could rest her head on the beds, providing an up close and personal experience. I didn't know if I could deal with making the hospital part of my stomping grounds, but she said I should give it some thought and I promised to do so.

Lynne had requested a parent's pass so I could go inside the ward. We made our way up to an eighth floor wing that was brightly lit. Wearing scrubs, we washed our hands carefully and covered our mouths with masks before going in. The process was in place because the infants were highly susceptible and special precautions had to be taken. Their weakened immune systems made them prone to infection and many were on respirators, fighting for their lives. Once the cleansing protocol had been completed, we went inside. Lynne pointed out several infants and spoke of their issues, but we stopped at only one isolette. She admired that baby for his courage and proceeded to tell me the infant had been born three months early. He was the first child born with his eyes fused to survive in New York State. Just yesterday, he had opened his left eye. When I put my hand into the isolette through the sterilized rubber glove attached to the otherwise sealed opening, he reached for it. He weighed two pounds, two ounces and held my pinkie as firmly as he could though his fingers did not reach around it entirely. When he did, his heartbeat quickened. Lynne accredited it to the power of human touch. As we stood in awe of this tiny man's desire to overcome the challenges associated with joining the world earlier than planned, his other eye opened. It was magical. Lynne said that moments like this were what she lived for and I understood why. For the first time, I truly saw how transformative human touch could be, but I guess I'd always known it. At that moment, I decided Molly and I would become a volunteer therapy dog team. I had so much to be thankful for. It would be wonderful to share the joy Molly brought to my life with others. She already knew how to be full-fledged good will ambassador and had cut her teeth doing just that for me.

When we parted, I told Lynne about my weekend plans. Paul had invited me for an idyllic country getaway and I had to get home early to prepare for it. The romantic feeling that prevailed after dinner, continued to build throughout the week and I was eager to see him the following morning. He had planned to pick me up early on Friday for a long weekend in the Berkshires. Lynne kindly volunteered to take care of Molly while I was away and would be staying at my place both nights. I packed sensibly, but dressed more nicely than I normally would have for a road trip, wearing the outfit that Ruth had given me. It had already worked some interview magic and maybe its mojo could work on Paul, to soften him up a bit more as well. Even though the temperature was brisk, Paul had driven over with the top down. The Mercedes had just been washed and it glistened in the fall morning sun. He suggested we stop for coffee before getting on the road and pulled over at the bus stop in front of Starbucks. As usual, he told me what to do, which was to stay in the car while he went inside. This time it was okay. I was actually glad that he went without me so Isaac wouldn't open his big trap and wreck the day. Given the opportunity, I was certain he would have. A lengthy line delayed Paul's return. After drinking coffee, I would certainly need to use the restroom. Knowing he wouldn't want to stop once we had gotten on the road, I grabbed the keys, got out of the car, and locked it before going inside. Paul had not ordered yet. When he noticed me, I whispered, "Figured I would hit the bathroom before we got on the road."

"I told you to stay in the car," he replied.

"Had you asked me instead of told me, I would have been happy to," I answered kissing him on the cheek before turning towards the ladies' room. "No worries. I locked it."

"That wasn't my concern. Besides, it's a convertible. Locking it does nothing."

When I returned, Paul was still waiting for our coffees and said, "Hurry outside before I get a ticket if somebody hasn't already stolen it."

Not a second later, he looked outside and called out, "Oh shit! They are towing my car."

His precious Mercedes was being hooked to a tow truck.

He ran outside and started yelling at the guy.

"What are you doing?"

"Towing a car parked illegally at a bus stop."

"It's half in the bus stop and I was only going to be a minute," he pleaded.

"Sorry, bro. That's like being a little pregnant, besides, even a minute would have been too long since you weren't driving a bus. Gotta do it."

Paul motioned for me join him. Hesitant to, I walked outside tentatively.

As I approached him, he commanded, "Jump in the car Julia. They can't tow it if you are in it."

I should have listened to my instincts instead of him and stayed inside. I stared blankly at him, without believing what he was asking me to do. Not knowing how to react, I stood frozen in the spot.

"JUMP IN THE CAR," he yelled angrily.

To this day, I'm not sure whether I was just trying to make amends for having left the car unattended, wanting to be helpful, longing to feel appreciated, or in a trance. Whatever the impetus was didn't really matter. What mattered was the fact that I complied.

People started gathering as the tow truck guy tried to reason with me. I wondered what Paul, who never wanted to make a scene, thought of this now.

"Lady, are you crazy? If you don't get out of there, I'm gonna have to call the cops."

I stared hypnotically at the guy.

"Come on lady, please don't listen to your husband. Get outta there."

More people had assembled and several had started to shout their opinions. All I heard was the buzz of strangers screaming at me. Paul, the conductor of the chaotic symphony, just kept shouting, "You're doing the right thing." Others showed their support by yelling, "If you stay in there they can't take your car."

"It's not my car," I whispered to no one in particular without realizing that I was holding the keys. Onlookers assumed it was my vehicle and Paul was taking full advantage of that.

A patrol car casually making its rounds slowed to see what the ruckus was about. The young cop, looking like he thought he was about to make his first collar, stared at me hopefully but without understanding the situation.

I shrugged my shoulders and smiled weakly.

Paul yelled out, "You can't tow the car with her in it."

Cop A looked at his partner and asked, "That true?"

"Nope."

"What do we do?"

"We ask her very nicely to get out of the car once and if she doesn't comply, we cuff her, then tow her to the nuthouse for evaluation. After that, we impound her fancy car."

"Hold your ground lady. Stay in there," yelled a young woman wearing a shirt that said show up or shut up. She was clearly looking for a cause to feed her rebellious nature. Isaac, who apparently couldn't resist finding out what was happening, walked out with a fresh cup of coffee and handed it to me.

"Has it gotten so boring that you are role playing now? Julie, get out of there or you'll be drinking this in jail," he said convincingly.

Looking at Isaac, Cop B took the coffee from my hands and placed it in the cup holder. He handcuffed me to the steering wheel as he replied, "Too late for that buddy. I'm taking them both in. You can pick her up at Bellevue if her husband doesn't."

"Fuck," I heard Paul say under his breath as we were being hauled off. "Now I have to go post bail." Calling out loudly with bravado, he continued, "Do you know who I am?"

Without missing a beat, Cop B replied, "Say another word asshole and I'll take you in too since it seems you have amnesia and don't know who you are!"

They towed the car, with me cuffed to the steering wheel, down Broadway as the crowd's cheers faded farther away. It wasn't until that moment, that I acknowledged jumping into a car against my better judgment so the Svengali I was dating would like me more. It was ridiculous to have followed his direction blindly and I was just starting to understand the consequences of my actions.

I was the best-dressed patient in Bellevue wearing my $800 outfit and my Birkin style bag. The cops, who were already there, commented that they couldn't understand why a sane chick would allow herself to be cuffed to a car. When the attending nurse took one look at me, she asked the cops, "What's she in for, shoplifting on Madison Ave?"

"Nope," said B.

"This I gotta hear."

"This lovely woman got herself cuffed to the steering wheel of her husband's car so it wouldn't get towed."

"Seriously?"

"Yep. Doozy, huh?"

"He's not my husband," I said quietly.

"Man, I thought I'd seen everything. Alright sugar, go into the dressing room and strip. Put on this gown and I'll be there in a minute to perform my search."

"You're kidding me, right?"

"Do I look like I'm kidding?" she scowled at me. "Wish I was. I don't like doing this any more than you like having it done, trust me."

She gave me a minute to undress, then walked in without even looking at me.

"Got any drugs?"

"Drugs? No."

"Under the influence?"

"Of what?"

"Good question. That's exactly what I was wondering. Why'd you listen to your crazy ass husband and jump in the car?"

"He's not my husband," I responded loudly this time. "We were going away for our first romantic weekend together."

She chuckled under her breath "Romantic, yeah right. That's special. If you are not kidding, then you should pay the cops a reward. Sounds to me like you dodged a bullet with that asshole."

"Maybe. He is a little bit overbearing."

"A little bit, huh? You're a real trip, you know that. Speaking of romantic, I'm not gonna do a cavity search because I don't want to scare your crazy ass, but lady, honestly, get a brain and for God's sake, stand up for yourself. You can't listen to what every jerk thinks you should be doing. Come on, get dressed. We're done here."

I dressed quickly knowing she was right, but was too embarrassed to admit trying to win him over, even to myself. I walked out to find Paul just a few feet from the examining room with his back to me. I heard him ask, "Where is she?" and was secretly pleased that he was so concerned.

"Getting dressed," Cop A said pointing towards the nurse and me.

Paul looked over and said, "Not her. The car."

"Are you for real?" the stunned nurse asked him.

As I walked towards him, Paul looked at me and tried to cover up for his callousness, extending his open arms to me.

Blushing violently but acting as though nothing had happened, he said, "If we rush to get the car, we can still make it upstate before evening."

The nurse called out to me, "If you say yes, you are nuts and we'll have to keep you here for observation. You dress real well, but you have no taste in men sweetheart."

"Not on your life Paul," I replied strengthened by the color commentary that had been provided.

"Take that you asshole," my back up called out as the cops laughed.

"By the way, why didn't you jump in the car yourself?" the cop asked. He waited for Paul to answer for at least a full minute.

After thinking about it, Paul replied honestly, "I wasn't sure if I'd be arrested."

"Only in New York," the cop muttered.

The nurse handed me back my bag, the car keys, and my now cold coffee. I considered keeping the keys, but I thought better of it because that would only mean that I'd have to see him again. When I handed them to him, he looked at me and said, "Let's go sweetie. Say goodbye to your new friends."

"I'm not coming."

"Don't play around. It's not funny."

"I'm not playing."

"Julie you've got to be kidding. Stop grandstanding just because you have an audience. Come on."

I said nothing. He started to walk away, then turned back to me and said, "Chop, chop. You know how I hate to be late. Let's go."

I stood silently seething and ran through my options, certain that my response would either end the relationship for good or define it going forward.

"We don't have all day," he said impatiently tapping his foot. "Let's go Julia."

"I told you, I'm not going."

"We had plans. You can't just leave me hanging."

Cop B called out, "Listen to him. She can't leave him hanging. What a pip this guy is!"

Ignoring what they said, Paul called out, "Come on Julia. I care for you." I stared at him without answering. Then he said, "I get it. You just need a little time to cool off."

"Ten bucks says she'll go," Cop A called out.

The nurse took him up on the bet saying, "No way. Not after what he put her through. She sees he's a dick now." They were acting as though wagering on the outcome of a game, completely disregarding that we heard their entire voiceover.

Paul stood there in disbelief and giving in said, "Ok fine. When will I see you again?"

Asserting myself and realizing what a fool I had been, I replied, "You'll see me again when shit smells like Chanel."

My three fans stood and clapped. Regardless of whether it was the nurse's coaxing or that something had changed inside me, I had finally taken a step to respect myself and to be respected, probably for the first time in my life. It felt good to have a crowd cheering for me again that day, even if that time, it was only three people.

Paul was escorted out of my life by two cops. The nurse nodded as though acknowledging that I had made the right decision and at that moment, I knew my mom would have been proud of me.

It was still early and I was already halfway downtown, so I decided to go to the Department of Motor Vehicles to see what was needed to renew my license. At least I could get something productive accomplished that day. I knew the DMV was close by without knowing the exact location. After reading online, that if my license had not lapsed for more than a year, it could be renewed without any issue, I walked to the station to find out which subway would get me there.

As was the norm for a state agency, the line was out the door. I called Lynne to let her know that I would be home by dinnertime. She was really curious and wanted to hear what had happened. Rather than getting into the story in a public place, I told her that she would hear all about it later and assured her that the story was worth waiting for. Since I was coming home that afternoon, she decided to do some errands instead of staying with Molly and said we'd catch up at the shelter.

When the sign finally flashed my number, the guy behind the counter asked for my license. He was friendly. Obviously, he hadn't been on the job too long because he was still courteous. He didn't have that glazed "civil servant on the job" look. After staring at the screen for several minutes, he looked puzzled. He advised me that I had over $2,500 worth of unpaid parking violations that would need to be paid before I could renew my license.

I looked at him doubting the veracity of what he was saying, and asked, "How can that be when I don't even have a car? I hadn't driven in a couple of years until a week ago."

"When you got another ticket?"

"Yes," I replied knowing that the recent ticket didn't help my chances of being believed.

"Good question," he replied.

After calling his manager over to help unravel the ticket mystery, he informed me that my old Volkswagen, had been parked illegally in the Bronx, for almost six months, over a year ago. The car had been accumulating parking tickets until it was towed and junked. As though the morning hadn't been bad enough, I had this to deal with. I was watching every penny and the newly-discovered tickets amounted to what was a small fortune for me. The fines would put a huge deficit in my already tight budget.

The clerk and his manager looked at me disbelievingly while I explained the car's history. When I told them that my husband had kept it in the divorce and subsequently given it to his new girlfriend, apparently without transferring the title, they started listening more attentively. It appeared his gal pal must have done it to spite him, but instead, in bounced back on me. The two men looked at each other and conferred briefly. Then, they did something that should have gone down in the history books alongside the Immaculate Conception. The manager looked at me and said, "Lady, I don't know why, but I believe you. I've never done this before and don't anticipate ever doing it again, but here goes." He turned the computer screen around so I could see it and clicked delete several dozen times while I watched the tickets vanish one by one. Though it was still a few months early he said, "Merry Christmas Miss. Now pay your renewal fee, take care of your ticket by mail and get the hell out of here before I change my mind. If you tell anybody about this, I'll lose my job. So, forget about me, forget about your Volkswagen, and make believe today never happened. Go get your license and have a nice life."

I couldn't believe that two Department of Motor Vehicle employees had just done this for me. It shouldn't have been a part of their DNA. I imagined they had seen enough people across the counter that they were astute judges of human nature. Their actions rendered me speechless. When I tried to say thank you, the younger guy still at the window silenced me and assumed the civil servant stance. He slumped his shoulders, wore an expressionless face and droned, "That'll be $72.50." When I handed him my credit card he said, "You'll get your permanent license in the mail in about two weeks. Don't forget to pay your summons on time." Just to show me that he was still the same guy who had gotten the assist for Government workers, he gave me a quick smile and winked as he handed me my temporary license.

I left, grateful for my good fortune, and for the kindness of strangers. It felt as though the winds of luck were changing. I stopped at a newsstand before getting on the subway and purchased ten dollars' worth of lottery tickets to test my theory. Putting them in my pocket, I thought of a better use for them and went back to the DMV. I cut the line and went directly to the clerk who had helped me, handing him the tickets. "Good luck, my friend and thank you."

I thought about everything that had happened to me that eventful day as I walked to the subway. It had been a roller coaster of emotions with a feeling of uncertainty prevailing throughout. Feeling as though I had reached the summit of my unsettled year, with every aspect of my life in flux, I remembered something I hadn't thought about in quite a while. Maybe it had been the day's tumultuous ups and downs that triggered the memory. While in college, I used to go to the Coney Island boardwalk to clear the cobwebs from my mind. After spending time there, I would always return with a better vantage point on whatever was troubling me. It was already mid-afternoon and with no set plan, instead of going home, I decided it was time to make the trek again. Not knowing if the pilgrimage could still help bring my life more clearly into focus, I knew it was certainly worth a try. The irony was not lost on me, that the place where I was going to think about life, was a land of make-believe adventure.

I was a dreamer and after not having been there in years, thinking about the park made me feel young again. The Cyclone had once been the park's crown jewel, but since then, it had been destroyed by Hurricane Sandy. I remembered seeing images of the tall, splintered remains standing erect and defiant, a testament to its structural strength. Even though it had been beaten by the storm, its core stood. Vowing to come back, it had not surrendered.

Getting off the train, I envisioned the monster as the monolith I remembered and feared being sadly disappointed. I as walked towards the park, it was cold and damp. A fog had settled in and was starting to get denser. In the distance, I could see where the coaster had stood and saw its outline as in a dream. Through the fog, I imagined seeing its silhouette looming majestically large in the distance as though it had emerged from the ruins, its spirit intact.

The Cyclone came into view through the fog. It lurked ominously in the shadows as though in a memory, but it was real. It had been rebuilt after the storm, exactly as the original. The replica was a nod to its history, an acknowledgement that it had born witness to the passage of time. Even though I hadn't felt the pull of its powerful force in decades, its sheer size still humbled me. I always felt small in its presence.

I remembered how frightened I had been of riding it and wasn't certain what had scared me most about it. Perhaps it was the feeling of dropping so quickly from great heights, or the squeaking of the wooden supports as the metal cars made their way along the prematurely aged track, with hardware that was made rusty by the salty sea breeze.

It felt as though I was there by myself. I walked around for a few minutes in my private playground. As though being led by destiny, I ended up at the infamous wooden coaster just as the attendant was closing the ride. He looked at me, then at his watch and said, "The park is empty and it is closing time. Besides, it looks like rain and I'm going home to the missus."

Tears welled up in my eyes "What do you mean the park is empty? Don't I count?" I asked him quietly.

He smiled wistfully as though sensing my need and remembering the innocence and vulnerability of youth. He hesitated, then said, "Of course you count. Come here little girl, I guess we can take her out for one more ride today."

I quietly got in the first car, the terror car. Once the steel safety bar lowered, the attendant helped buckle me in. I could feel my heart thumping so loud that I was sure he heard it when he asked if I was ready. Certain I would not be able to find my voice, I nodded my response. As he walked back to the power switch, my hands clenched the safety bar. It started slowing making its way up the long steep climb. It made the trek begrudgingly. Approaching the crest of the first ascent, the car stalled for what seemed like a lifetime as my heart beat rapidly in my throat. I looked down at the world around me. As though to heighten my fear, it paused, reverberating, so I could drink in the danger.

I thought about the fear that had immobilized me since the divorce - fear of being alone, fear of losing my job, fear of getting old and of not being loved. Every one of these dreaded things had come to fruition and yet, here I was. Life wasn't perfect, but living in terror was much more debilitating than being present in the reality.

I heard the sleeping giant awaken once again and knew that its next breath would signal the start of the descent. Just like wearing a certain fragrance could bring to life the memory of a wonderful night, being afraid took me back to a time when I was a young girl and my Dad brought me here. To keep me company, he rode the wooden monster so I wouldn't have to go alone. He hated rides and although he threw up twice when it was over, it didn't stop him from riding with me again, saying that adventures were always more fun when shared.

The feeling of controlled fear was an exhilarating one for me. Instantaneously, it reminded me of what it was like to be brave and of how much easier it was to stand up to challenges when one felt loved and secure. The monster bucked beneath me and I knew it would start its downward trajectory in a heartbeat like an elevator reeling out of control after the cables had been cut. I raised my hands to the sky as if in prayer, with hopeful defiance, and embraced the memory as it began its frighteningly high-speed descent. I screamed as loudly as I could, knowing no one could hear or rescue me. The drop left me breathless as the metal railings on wood produced a screeching sound that deafened me when the car turned for the next climb. With each ascent, I gulped deeply as though taking my last breath, but each time, more breaths followed. By the fifth climb, I had settled in and was enjoying the ride, laughing and loving the thrill of it. Realizing it could not defeat me, it sighed a last sound as it turned the bend and came to a stop. My emotions were garbled. I felt like a child again, hopeful and unfettered but not naïve anymore. I stood shaking with resolve and feeling empowered.

Realizing I hadn't paid the man, I walked towards him and asked how much I owed him. He looked at me knowingly as though understanding my journey and said, "If you are a millionaire, you owe me a million. If not, just a smile will do." I thanked him for indulging me and heard him mumble that he hoped his wife would understand.

I don't remember getting on the train to Manhattan but somehow found myself in front of Lincoln Center. I stood there taking it all in, back in the world of adults, a woman different from the one who had left in the morning. As I walked up Broadway towards my building, I caught a glimpse of myself in a plate glass window. Even I had to laugh at how I disheveled I looked after a trying day and a damp, windblown ride. In my mind, I resembled a Dali - melting and dripping all at once with raw emotion. I gave myself a nod, as an affirmation of what was truly important and welcomed back a part of me that had died years ago.

As I reconciled the day's events, it became evident that my view of the world had been altered. Even challenges happened for a reason. The setbacks had put me back on the path that fate had paved. Changes had taken place almost imperceptibly over the year, allowing me the time to adjust and the space needed to see things more clearly. I embraced the resilience of the human spirit while acknowledging the healing properties of time. They were steps in the right direction and I decided a celebratory cup of coffee was called for to mark the occasion.

Overdressed and exhausted, I popped into Starbucks knowing that Isaac would have something to say about how I looked, but it didn't matter. Time and again, for every asshole that was out there mucking it up, there was a good person standing in the wings ready to step in. It was just a matter of figuring out who played who in the western since they weren't wearing hats. I heard someone call my name and assuming it was Isaac, braced myself for a nasty remark before turning to confirm who was calling me.

It was Luke. It did my heart good to see him and I wondered why Ruth hadn't mentioned that he would return so soon. I moved back several places in the long line, happy to join him. His warm smile echoed my sentiments and acknowledged an unspoken appreciation for each other. There was an easy way about him that allowed me to be myself in his company.

"I'm glad you are here. Coffee isn't as enjoyable when you are alone," he told me. I remembered his mom had said something similar to me once and it had made me wonder why I couldn't meet a man like her.

We chatted casually while waiting to place our order. At the register, without even asking what we were having, Isaac handed us real cups instead of paper. I wondered why he handed Luke a cappuccino with a heart drawn in the foam and me a cup of brilliant, red tea. When I looked at Isaac inquisitively, he shrugged his shoulders and said, "Maybe it's time to get rid of the throwaways." Even he seemed different that day.

Luke and I took a small table in the corner. Sinking into my chair, I told Luke about my crazy day and attempted to make sense of the many different emotions that were bubbling up in me. He listened attentively, visibly untangling my thoughts without interjecting comments and seemed to understand the magnitude of what had taken place. I thought perhaps I had said too much and felt naked, waiting for him to comment. He did not pass judgment or offer solutions. Instead, Luke said, "Boy, the old lady is rubbing off on you. You are an old soul in a young body and wise beyond your years, truly a welcome change from the women I meet these days."

I smiled and accepted the compliment, thanking him without pausing to question why he was talking about meeting women again if he was married.

"I guess she has. It's funny how much life teaches you along the way when you stop to listen. Tell me about you. What are you doing back here so soon?"

"I've just bought an old house on the North Shore that needs lots of TLC and I'm looking forward to working on it. I closed on it during my last trip here. I have always loved working with my hands and I'm excited to see the fruits of my labor. It feels wonderful to be back home."

"I didn't know you had moved. Has your wife ever lived on the East Coast before?"

"My wife? I've been divorced for several years. I stayed out west because my business was there, but it never was the right fit. The time feels ripe to make a change and I am going to start consulting here. Up to now, I've dedicated my life to building a company's business and to making others wealthy. Now, I've had enough of being a company man. It's time to hang up the suit and make time to enjoy my own life."

First, I remembered thinking he was Ruth's date, then that he was married. How I struggled to divert my gaze that night! I avoided looking at him again that afternoon for fear of divulging the hopeful feelings that had surfaced as we spoke. Instead, I looked at the tag on my teabag to see what kind of tea the fragrant blend was. It was called Passion. I smiled thinking about the many times Isaac had interjected commentary on my life throughout the year, and silently hoping that the tea was indicative of what the future held.

Luke looked at his watch and said he was late for something. He was meeting his brother at the house in an hour and they were picking up supplies to work on it together. "I've got to run. There is lots to do before a housewarming party in two weeks. Nothing big or fancy, just a few people who are important to me, creating new memories."

Our conversation had come to a natural conclusion. When we stood, both of us seemed hesitant to leave. He said, "I'm sorry that I have to leave so quickly. I really enjoy your company."

So, I wasn't imagining it.

"I hope the rest of your day is uneventful. You deserve a relaxing evening after the day you had," Luke said hugging me warmly. He walked towards the door and stopped. Instead of opening it, he turned around and came back to where I was finishing my tea. "Would you join me for coffee in the morning?" he asked more shyly than I would have expected. Of course, I said yes. When we said goodbye for the second time, there was no remorse. We would see each other for a coffee date the following morning.

I had to laugh and shake my head at what life and Isaac had served up that day. After a year of drinking lots of coffee, going on many meaningless dates, and learning a multitude of things in the most unorthodox ways, I realized that for me, life was what occurred in the day to day. It happened in small snippets of learning and feeling, not in grand gestures. It felt as though the life I had lived until then was just practice for the one ahead.

I climbed the stairs two at a time, eager to see Molly and walk with her. Outside, the sunset had transformed the sky into a gorgeous tapestry of muted rose and plum tones. We walked to the park enjoying the crisp fall weather. I looked out over the great lawn to the water-colored heavens with promise and hope. The wind was picking up, swirling around me, and it felt good to be alive again.

As we walked home, the sun went down, closing the chapter on my eventful day. Before going upstairs, I opened the mailbox. Inside was a stack of mail with an envelope on top that didn't look like a bill. Smiling at no one in particular, I looked at it more closely and saw a handwritten return address that was not familiar to me. The seal showed it was mailed from Oyster Bay. I ran my index finger over the lettering, feeling the purposeful penmanship of the writer and laughed when I wondered what an expert would have seen in it.

Once inside, I left the mail on the table unopened. It would still be there tomorrow. I had something more important to do. I got my step stool and reached into storage space over the closet in search of old photographs. It took some time to locate the right box. Once it was in hand, I sat on the couch browsing through the pictures with

Molly's head on my lap. Many had actually held up well and I smiled at the memories they made real again. I found several of family and friends, as well as some beautiful landscapes to decorate the living room. Luke had the right idea about creating a space that would welcome new memories. I embraced the past, taking what was good from it to carry forward and setting aside the rest. Though it was still early, I was tired and allowed myself the luxury of surrendering to sleep, knowing that the next day would offer the opportunity to embark on a new beginning and appreciating that I was finally home.

EPILOGUE

So, after a year of dates and discovery, what have I learned? I've learned the coffee commandments for a happy life.

- Live in the moment and enjoy the ride
- Trust your instincts and your true friends
- Drink regular coffee - decaf sucks
- Open your heart and close your mouth
- Live your life with passion
- Rescued dogs return the favor
- Check your license on your birthday
- Successes are like rabbits – they breed a lot
- Keep learning throughout your life
- Don't let fear paralyze you
- Never make liver & onions on a first date
- Gray is beautiful and so is experience
- You can't microwave love
- Newer is not always better
- The shiniest penny is not worth any more
- Don't let your mistakes define you
- Agendas should be written in pencil
- Each day offers a chance to begin anew
- At first, it's tough to tell the cowboys from the villains when they are not wearing hats
- Nothing beats good cannelloni
- Sometimes, life's greatest lessons can come from the most unexpected places
- Trust should be earned, not given freely
- It's the guys who can tell you the things you don't want to hear, that are the keepers
- Catch curiosity and spread it
- Shit will never smell like Chanel
- And of course, don't judge a book by its cover

Made in the USA
Columbia, SC
17 June 2018